The Lotus and the Tiger

Lizzy Shortall.

The Lotus and the Tiger

Published by The Conrad Press in the United Kingdom 2021

Tel: +44(0)1227 472 874
www.theconradpress.com
info@theconradpress.com

ISBN 978-1-913567-94-1

Copyright © Lizzy Shortall, 2021

Printed and bound in Great Britain by Clays Ltd, Elcograf S.p.A

Typesetting and Cover Design by The Book Typesetters,
www.thebooktypesetters.com

The Conrad Press logo was designed by Maria Priestley.

The Lotus and the Tiger

A novel based on true events

Lizzy Shortall

Dedicated to Lar Coombes, a kind, funny and wise soul. My big brother who still looks after, guides and loves me from the spirit world. To anyone who is hurting or struggling right now. May we all be well. May we all be happy, may we all be peaceful and at ease.

PROFESSOR KIRKE:
Well, if she's not mad and she's not lying, then logically we must assume she's telling the truth.

PETER:
You're saying that we should just believe her?

PROFESSOR KIRKE:
She's your sister isn't she? You're a FAMILY. You might just try acting like one.

From *The Chronicles of Narnia. The Lion, the Witch and the Wardrobe* (1950)

by C.S. LEWIS

1

*H*ot blood sprayed me like warm water, blinding me and causing my hair to clump. I could taste it. I was too numb to gag. I do not know how long I stood there, staring at myself in the hut window before I realised it was my own reflection.

For a long time, I loved looking ten years younger than my actual age but now I looked every day of thirty-six.

I lifted my arm and tried to rub the blood off my neck. It just spread further. There was an uncomfortable ringing in my ears and reality winded me. He looked dead.

I began whispering prayers for him and for me. His family would miss him. I might miss him. It seemed absurd that it was possible to miss the being that held me hostage from my beautiful life.

I decided early on in life that I was not that bad and not too good at most things. I developed a 'fake it 'til you make it' attitude.

During the first three years in secondary school my friends and I laughed our way in huddles along the convent school corridors.

For the next three years I took to skipping classes and staying at home with Mam or with my best friend Brona. She was one year older than me. We pretended to be sisters, even though we looked nothing alike.

She has beautiful blonde hair and green eyes and freckles on her nose. I have blue eyes, strawberry blonde hair, rosy cheeks, and a big chocolate freckle in the middle of my left temple.

We were outside a lot on the big round green in my cul-de-sac or in Brona's fancy house. It was two minutes up a lane from mine. All I had to say was that I had an afternoon of religion classes and I got to skip school. The deal Mam often made with me was: 'If you peel the potatoes for dinner I won't tell your Daddy.'

She was gentle with big brown eyes and round features and she believed any lie I told her. She smelled like Rich Tea biscuits, not that sweet, but pleasant.

Mam had a naivety that not many adults can maintain. She grew up in a Dublin family with ten siblings. She was the type of person to go along with things. She always wore a lot of turquoise eyeshadow and a lick of burgundy lipstick.

She went to bed every night with a head full of rollers. For a woman with five children she looked well, a pretty woman. In our younger years she was funny. The chat bubbled out of her. She tried to get Dad chatting with her. He was too busy watching television, reading his papers and books or going to bed early.

Except for the weekends he spent more time with us, playing Abba songs loudly on a Saturday morning. We took turns standing on the kitchen table dancing with him.

Mam spent the evenings with us, in particular with my older brother Shane and me. He was six years older than me. They often discussed philosophical subjects Dad had no interest in.

During those animated years with her, the house seemed brighter. She changed gradually. Those fun years were followed by a quietness with her seeming sad. She occasionally voiced how she was desperate for more in her life. 'You know there was a solicitor who wanted to marry me, I could have had a different life with him.'

There was an air of regret from Mam about marrying Dad, like she wished she was with someone different. A man that would go to the cinema or theatre.

Over the years her eyes slowly became less engaging and a darker brown that reflected a distant look. It was like looking in a window at night where you cannot see in and you cannot tell if whoever is on the other side can see out. I often ended up feeling unheard and unwitnessed.

On occasion she brightened up and she was almost visible again. Similar to a shadow that keeps disappearing, she would eventually fade away.

Dad was easily irritated by us children. In particular he seemed most angered by Shane and me. He made it clear that we were 'too bloody sensitive.'

We often arrived home from school to Mam in bed or under a blanket on the couch. Her curls poking out, half asleep watching snooker or the *Oprah Winfrey Show.*

I found her voice soothing. I loved her way of helping people to find ways to be happy after terrible things happened to them. I watched Oprah as much as possible with Mam. She lit a fire of hope in my belly and gave me comfort.

Every day I went to sleep and woke to the sound of Mam rattling an old baby formula tin full of medication. I tried desperately to help her figure out what would make her happier and I never could.

She was a stay-at-home mam looking after my two brothers, two sisters, and me. We seemed too much for her. I was the youngest girl and Dan was the youngest boy, ten months younger than me.

Dad paid all the bills, went to work daily and ran all the finances. He used to give Mam her 'wages' in cash weekly. She liked to shop.

I continued on during my teenage years and my twenties trying to help Mam. If she felt better that would mean I did not have to feel guilty when I left her alone or when I was happy.

She seemed so lost and hard to reach. I tried to get through to her. I firmly believed for many years that she would find happiness.

She had a pattern of plodding along unhappily, giving out. Countless times I accompanied her to the local supermarket, on the way she would repeat the same script,

'Your Daddy would prefer be in the pub on a Saturday with his brother and those slappers. He doesn't even wear his wedding ring.'

Once or twice a year she exploded. I remember hearing, 'I can't take any more of you I'm leaving. I've had enough.'

She packed her red suitcase and left to stay with my aunty numerous times, quietly crying. Returning a couple of days later acting like nothing happened.

When I was twelve-years-old and my sister Paula was thirteen, Mam told us she had been in psychiatric hospitals. The staff put her in a wrought iron cot bed she was not capable of getting out of.

They gave her electroconvulsive treatment too. Mam said

she escaped from the hospital. She walked by reception in her clothes to come back and see us five children.

She told me, 'I did not get to hold you or see you, Lucy, for the first three months of your life. Nobody brought you up to me. If I cried, they just gave me more medication.'

This scared the shite out of Paula and me. I started to experience anxiety. I suppose that is another word for fear.

At fourteen-years-old I was standing at the top of the stairs at home. Shane arrived home from a trip to Amsterdam. He was in the porch wearing an oversized brown coat. The buttons had been swapped for massive red buttons and his hair was in dreadlocks. I could see big gulps of water flowing from his eyes.

He resembled a homeless man dressed as the saddest clown imaginable. I had no idea what was happening to him, my favourite person in the whole world.

Mam and Dad left with him and came back without him. They said he took too many drugs in Amsterdam. He had drug-induced psychosis. He was going to be in the psychiatric hospital for a while.

It was miles away in the country and we were not allowed to visit him or to tell anyone where he was. Mam's stories about psychiatric services were etched into my mind with indelible ink. *Oh God no, not those places where they tie people down in big cots and inject them with too much medication.*

In that moment a ball of anxiety latched on within me and whirled at high speed for many years to come. Occasionally as a small ball and other times a large mass of nervous energy. On bad days it grew tentacles that wriggled out in every direction within my body.

I tried to get on with going to school and seeing my friends but I missed Shane. My parents did not tell the rest of us anything else except he would be back when he was better.

Meanwhile Brona and I created our own excitement. She was besotted with one of the local boys. His friend from another estate took a shine to me. He had a shaved head and a long blond fringe slicked back.

Brona and her new crush facilitated notes between me and him. The four of us arranged to go to the local disco in a school hall. At age fourteen we were all underage but in we marched. There was moshing and messing and drinking.

After a while he and I had enough, we went outside, we were right beside a park so in we went. I was not afraid with him holding my hand. That was all we did; it was innocent and sweet.

We talked and laughed before we walked back to the disco. It was 1am and everyone had gone home. We walked to Brona's house and threw pebbles at her window. There was no sign of her.

We went to our other friend's house and looked in the sitting room window. There were no lights on there either. It was now 2am. I knew Dad would kill me altogether if I arrived home so late.

We walked around the village, arriving at my primary school grounds. We went in and sat on the freezing cold ground talking for hours.

At 6am I needed to pee. We decided to go to the lane at the back of my house. I left my blond buddy there waiting. I ran back around to the front of the house and went in the door. I snuck up the stairs.

Halfway back down, the kitchen door opened. It was Dad. I forgot he worked some Saturdays. He was getting ready to leave.

He barked at me, 'What are you doing?'

'Brona and I were delivering a Valentine's Day card and I had to pee.'

'Have you been out all night, Lucy?'

He was studying my face for any flicker of guilt.

'No, Dad, I stayed in Brona's.'

'Right. Get up to bed now.'

I had to think on my feet, my buddy was out the back waiting.

'Brona thinks I am coming back.'

Dad walked towards the front door.

'Well, go and tell her you are not coming back. Now.'

He sat in his car outside, facing the lane to Brona's house. I scurried up the lane. I stood there, talking to no one, trying to judge how long the non-existent conversation should take. Then I ran back.

As he drove off, I belted out the back and told my blond buddy I had to get to bed. He hurried off and I went to bed thinking I had gotten away with it.

The next morning, I relayed the same tale to Mam and my sisters. Before I got Paula on her own to tell her the true story there was a knock at the front door.

Mam was washing the dishes and I was drying them, wearing my pyjamas. I answered the door. A woman I never saw before asked me in a gruff Dublin accent,

'Are you Lucy?'

'Yes.'

'Is your ma home?'

Mam appeared behind me, drying her hands on her slacks.

'Eh, Hello?' Her voice was unsure and nervous.

'Are you aware your daughter was out with my son all last night?'

'Oh no, Lucy stayed in her friend's house last night.'

As she said it she looked to me as if to say, *tell her*. I looked at the ground with my cheeks burning, wishing I was at least dressed for this ordeal.

'You better come in.' Mam sounded worried. The three of us sat in the sitting room. Mam looked from me to this stranger.

'Listen, love, he didn't tell on you, if that's what you are thinking. I had to beat it out of him.'

I had an image of his pretty face all bashed up and I started to cry. 'We went for a walk; we did not think the disco would be over. It was too late to come home so we sat in the school grounds.'

Mam looked at me wide-eyed with worry. She was way out of her depth to deal with this scary woman.

It may have been due to Mam's gentle and quiet nature as the woman left as quickly as she came. I think she wanted to see who her son was hanging around with.

Mam told my sisters and the questions started to fly. Paula, looking afraid, asked Mam, 'Are you going to tell Dad?'

'I'll have to tell your Daddy,' Mam said while glancing at me. I got a lump in my throat.

'Please don't tell him, he will go mad.'

Mam bargained with me. 'I'll wait until after he has had his dinner, but I'll have to tell him.'

We all knew he was always in better form after he was fed. I waited for the sound of his car pulling up outside. The engine stopped. The front door opened. My heart was thudding in my ears as he arrived into the kitchen smiling with a box of Roses chocolates for Mam.

I disappeared out of there up to my bedroom. I was praying that he would eat his dinner and take it well. I began nervously tidying the room.

The girls in the family had to clean, hoover, and polish every Saturday morning. He would inspect it when he got back from work.

I thought if my bedroom room was neat, he might go easier on me. I was kneeling on the floor, making my bed when I heard him booting up the stairs. She told him before dinner.

My bedroom door flung open. I had no time to stand up. He towered over me, shouting,

'You little bitch. Who do you think you are making a show of us? You little slapper.'

I cowered on the floor.

'If I could, I'd give you a good beating.' Out he stormed as if to prevent himself from doing so. I stopped breathing; I was so scared. I did not dare move.

Later Mam came up and said he wanted me. I went down to the sitting room. She stayed outside; I stood barely inside the door, afraid there may be the threatened beating on the way.

Not removing his gaze from the television, he asked 'Do you need to get a pregnancy test or anything?'

I was mortified that he asked me such a thing. *We held hands, we did not even kiss.* I was so embarrassed and upset. I kept thinking *who? Or what does he think I am? Oh yes, a slapper.*

I managed to mumble, 'No, Dad.'

'Well, you are grounded for three weeks.'

I was surprised to hear that. None of us had ever been grounded before.

'Do you hear me?' He was getting angry again.

'Ok.'

I waited to see if he would say anything else. He did not, so I backed out of the room. I felt afraid to turn my back in case he pounced.

Over the coming days if he was home, I stayed in my bedroom. Shane was still in hospital, whenever they went to visit him, I went out to hang around with Brona and our friends.

I told her they were visiting an old aunt in hospital. My crush had apparently tried to run away and had been sent to live with his dad in Wicklow.

That night I told God or Jesus or whoever he was, I was not sure, where to go. I am abashed to admit I told him from my fourteen-year-old bed, *fuck you; just go fuck off. What good are you to me if this is what you let happen?'*

I was angry at him for not looking out for me better and for letting Shane be in that psychiatric hospital. I did not dare tell Dad to fuck off, so I told the other Almighty.

I cried alone inconsolably. Normally in these situations I had Shane to turn to. Poor Shane was in some mad place and I missed him terribly.

After six weeks he got out of hospital. I was ungrounded by then. He moved into a bedsit in Dublin. I wondered did he blame Mam and Dad for putting him in the hospital.

I wanted to give him a big hug, but I was unsure if he knew I was aware he had been in the hospital. His clown coat had vanished, and he was his old self. No one mentioned his time in the psychiatric hospital again at family occasions.

My expedition with the blond-haired boy was mentioned again. A lot. In fact, it shaped the course of my relationship with my parents for the following two years. I was branded as 'wild' after staying out all night with 'Night Rider.' The whole family referred to him as that.

For those couple of years my parents doubted my overnight plans. They questioned if I was telling the truth.

By the time I was sixteen or seventeen it was back to no one noticing what I was up to, which was mostly underage drinking in Dublin city with Brona and some school friends at the weekends.

We went back to school on a Monday and waited for Friday to come around. I gazed out the window, unable to concentrate mostly due to worrying over Mam.

Other days I did anything to have a giggle. The nuns insisted we had to wear our white socks pulled up to our knees and keep our white blouse top buttons closed. Our ties had to be perfectly in place and our name tags needed to be in the correct position on our navy jumpers. There were many rules to be obeyed.

My eldest sister, Kerry, ten years older than me, had rubbed some of the teachers up the wrong way. Her reputation was a black mark against my name in advance of the teachers knowing me. Two of them seemed to take an instant dislike to me.

If I disobeyed them in some small way, such as by not having my name tag on, they shouted at me and called me Kerry Woodrow accidentally. It was our distinctive surname that was the giveaway. I resented her for this. In comparison to the pain Kerry would cause me later in life this was nothing.

People threaded lightly around my other sister Paula, so as not to induce the crying. I got the brunt of Dad's fast tongue. He acted as if Paula might fall apart if anyone upset her.

His skinny and sharp features were barely disguised by his fluffy beard. He charmed other people outside the house with his Santa Claus smile.

Dad left school at fourteen years of age and had a big chip on his little shoulder. If he was in a bad mood, he asked us, 'Are you people thicks or are you fools?'

He educated himself over the years with a lot of reading. Dad was mostly well-informed and sometimes ill-behaved. I was never sure what might cause him to get angry. He made my heart go ninety with his shouting and threats of 'a thump' or 'a smack in the chops.'

During his outbursts we all scarpered to different hiding places in the house. It was always me he managed to find and slap.

When Paula, Dan and I were out in the back garden as very small children if one of us started to cry he automatically blamed and punished me. Even without seeing what happened I was the one to get his harsh tongue or the smack.

I learned from a young age not to push him too far. At five-years-old I was kneeling one evening, using a soft footrest as a table to do my homework on. I rubbed a hole in the page while trying to practice my letters. Dad was standing over me and he gave me a full force slap across my face for my mistake.

I was devastated. If we had an argument, he bought me a packet of Maltesers to say sorry. This time it was a box of them.

2

In secondary school I still cringed if I had to show Dad schoolwork. On a Friday I had to line up, hiding behind Paula and Dan waiting for him to sign our spelling tests.

He would get angry at my low spelling test marks. I started to equate being able to spell directly with how intelligent I was.

As my academic confidence shrank over the years my giddiness grew. If Dad upset me, I ran to Shane. He was six foot one, I am five foot one. He seemed even taller to me back then. Shane had green eyes and brown busy hair. His smile shined kindness at me in beams.

He seemed to know if I was upset by Dad. I literally used to cry on his shoulder and by his mere presence I felt safer.

On one occasion Shane found me crying on my bedroom floor. He brought me into his room and played some music for me. It was Bob Marley's song 'Three Little Birds'. By the final chorus he had me singing and smiling with him, *Don't worry about a thing, cause every little thing is gonna be alright.*

Dad was predictable at the weekends because he binge drank then. He came home on a Saturday evening as a happy drunk with tales of a better life for us all. When the hangover kicked in he was easily annoyed.

I was never truly comfortable in his company and definitely not when he had been drinking. Still to this day I cannot bear the smell of Guinness.

Paula and I used to give each other knowing looks, while staying quiet and a safe distance from him. She seemed to live in fear of him too. Yet simultaneously she had him on a pedestal.

Paula made sure to do well at school, often heading out the door with her school bag on her back, as I was coming down the stairs after getting out of the bed. Tired after staying up late listening to Mam's woes.

Paula was the meekest of all us children and Dad controlled her the most easily. Mam made a point of repeatedly telling me 'Paula is your Daddy's favourite.' She seemed envious of their relationship. I told myself that I was her favourite.

Dad's other beloved was Dan, the favoured son by far. Dad approved that Dan had a short haircut and that he lived for rugby, winning many medals. Dad covered half of the hallway with them.

I did not mind. I liked Dad as much as he liked me, which was not much. I think he knew too.

Paula wanted us to be richer than we were. She was horrified by some of the antics Dan, and I got up to. She used to correct Dan for sounding 'too Dublin.'

We rolled our eyes at this. Dan told her, 'That's because *I am* from Dublin.'

He was not one to say how he was feeling. If he went quiet at home, I knew to give him space. We both knew it was not easy being part of our family.

He was Phibsborough's version of Brian O'Driscoll. He played rugby relentlessly and was top class at it. He had a wild streak too. He went from robbing the neighbour's orchards to stealing tyres from the local garage. He got caught with some of his friends. Dad went easy on him, which was good. Of

course, I noted the difference in his tolerance of our misde-
meanours.

Dad disapproved of Shane, his long hair, his hippy clothes and his music. He frowned upon him and his dreadlocks. He made no attempts to hide it. He told him that he was 'dirty and lazy.'

Shane was tall, but after Dad tore strips off him he often left the house seeming smaller, with tears and anger in his eyes.

One night Dad was giving us a lift to the cinema. They had a big row and Dad shook his fist in Shane's face. We jumped out of Dad's car and I tried to console Shane by telling him, 'loads of dads do not get on with their sons.'

'I know Lucy, its ok.' Shane looked sad. It was not ok, and he was not ok. We watched the film in silence. Shane still pale with the fright.

He was the most intelligent and kindest soul in my life. He breezed through school and went travelling aged seventeen. I wished I could go too.

As a young teenager I idolized him. He was a vegetarian, so I was too. He liked the Doors and Bob Dylan, so I did too. His room was filled with books. He seemed cool, with all his travelling tales and the music he introduced the rest of us to.

There was always music playing at home. This lightened the tension. Except on a Sunday morning, it was usually a bit less uplifting.

When Dad was gone to visit his family, while Mam was peeling the potatoes in the kitchen, she would play that song *Crazy* by Patsy Cline. Singing along, *Crazy, I'm crazy for feeling so lonely, I'm crazy, crazy for feeling so blue, I knew, you'd love me as long as you wanted and then someday, you'd leave me for somebody new.*

She seemed so lonely, crying into the potatoes. She was looking after us five children all alone, all week with no adult company. She seemed alone, even when Dad was there too, always waiting for his attention.

In secondary school I became accustomed to anxiety being a constant companion because of the way some of the teachers behaved. Similar to Dad they scared me into submission.

My school days were made enjoyable by visits to and from my lovely Aunty Clare. She had the best job in the universe: she worked in a bakery. She arrived at our house every Thursday evening with little white boxes full to the brim of jam donuts, cream slices, iced buns and chocolate eclairs.

On school holidays, Paula and I pleaded with Mam to go home with her for a night. Sometimes Brona came with us too. Aunty Clare lived in an old Georgian town house in Dublin City with her husband Brendan. He was a gentle man.

At age fourteen, Brona and I graduated from eating cakes and 'borrowing' paper pounds from our mams' purses for Cola Cubes and Tayto crisps to borrowing something more exciting, their alcohol.

Initially I did not even enjoy the taste of alcohol. I did like that it made me less shy. The first time we drank I took two cans of Ritz from under Mam's nose.

Our debut was on the sea front on a cold Saturday night. I drank the two cans quickly. Soon I was lying on a bench, half awake and half asleep.

Brona and Hilary, my other best friend from school, managed to get me into a taxi. It was two cans, but being a small fourteen-year-old, it did not take much.

From then on, we regularly raided Brona's mam's drink cabinet. It was always full of rum, vodka and whiskey. We used to hold our noses to avoid the taste as we drank straight from the bottles. It tasted strong and burned the back of my throat. It made me gag.

This got us drunk fast. Happily heading off to discos with badly applied orange make up and, in my case, often ending in a black out. According to my friends I appeared as if I knew everything that was going on. I was 'extra happy and loved everyone.'

One weekend we managed to get some Baileys too. I guzzled so much of it that soon after I arrived at the underage disco, I was not even able to stand. The security men threatened to phone my parents.

Brona managed to get Shane on my parents' landline and told him to come and collect me. Shane got me going and walked me around the block to sober me up. He sneaked me into our house to the bathroom to vomit, before he put me to bed.

The next morning, he warned me to be careful. Dad was asking questions. He heard every pin drop and suspected I was up to something. I vaguely remembered the walk. Shane told him I had a dodgy curry.

Despite blacking out and vomiting I liked that the drink helped me to put on a happy face to hide the misery I was carrying inside me. Mam continued to offload all sorts of unhappy thoughts on me on many evenings.

I felt guilty going out on a Saturday night, knowing she was alone and lonely. The cider bubbles pushed down all those sad and guilty feelings. I put on the happy face and headed out to the sea front, church grounds, local disco or night clubs. I made sure I brought my new friend cider.

Mam's Misery was always waiting for me. At the edge of a dance floor, when I got home or the next morning. There she was, Misery, resembling a grey figure, a misty energy that permeated anywhere.

Misery followed me into rooms. Even though I shut the door tight it seeped in under it and through the keyhole. If I stopped drinking, it would surround me and envelope me, until the sadness pushed past the cider bubbles and tears came.

I pretended to friends I was fine. I would get a tequila to enter blackout oblivion. *Lucy the happy drunk.* I had no idea what problems pushing down my emotions with alcohol would cause me later in life.

I did the minimum at school and got an average Leaving Certificate. I expended my energy on giggling and messing rather than studying.

Reality hit that I had not obtained enough points for any college. I applied to do a Post Leaving Certificate (PLC) Community Studies course. Brona was already on her second year of a secretarial course when I began mine.

I instantly loved the course yet I often had a knot in my stomach in the group of classmates. Before long I made some good friends. Despite a lot of partying with them, I was good at the course.

I loved sociology and psychology. I got distinctions. When I mentioned my good marks Dad concluded,

'Ah, she is doing well because she fancies her lecturer.' I was horrified.

Paula went to Chicago for the summer that year with her friends. I missed her. We almost had a telepathic relationship and spoke regularly on the phone.

I got a new part-time job in a theatre in the city centre working in the bar and at the plays as an usher. Brona and a girl who I had known in school, Sissy, were working there too. Sissy and I got close quickly, partying after work every weekend.

I was busy on a work experience placement, as part of my course as a social care worker. After I finished the course, I worked there for one year until Paula invited me to go to Australia. She was going with two of her friends for one year on a working holiday via Thailand.

I did not hesitate for even one second. I was super excited and requested a leave of absence from the organisation. I vaguely remember the goodbye party and waking up in my co-worker's house. I was mortified, not remembering how I got there and discovering I had vomited on her floor.

I did the walk of shame, feeling still drunk, walking through the city to the bus stop in her oversized clothes. I was glad I was not going to have to see her again for one year.

Once I was on the plane to Australia that incident was long forgotten, and we were on the wine. Paula's friends were different to mine. They sipped their drinks and cheated by eating.

If Sissy was there, we would have been ordering tequila. She would have been smoking joints in the toilet. This tamer crew probably saved me from myself. As it was the year in

28

Australia was one very long party. With me at the centre of every single session.

I managed to travel around seeing stunning sunsets and sunrises and even ran a backpacker's hostel for a while. I made new friends with other backpackers and travelled along the East Coast with them.

It seemed abrupt when one year later Paula and I were in Dad's car on route back from the airport. As the old familiar roads whizzed by my window, I wondered why I did not stay in Australia.

The unchanged landscape of north Dublin flew by me out the car window. Mam was in the front beside Dad. Her hair was greyer, but everything else was the same.

The reunion with Dan, Shane, Kerry and her children was lovely. Dad still had that knack of making me feel like I was doing something wrong. After the initial novelty of having us home from the other side of the world, he returned to his irritable self.

Before we left for Australia, he told us to pack up all our belongings because they were selling the family home. Yet they did not, and all our stuff was in brown boxes in our bedroom. It was not exactly welcoming and soon enough neither was he.

It was relief while I was in Australia to not have to put up with him justifying his bad behaviour as a joke or because he was angry.

Within in a couple of months of being back in his house, I announced I was moving to London, to stay with some English friends I met in Australia. Mam broke down in tears.

'What age are you now?' was Dad's response.

'I'm twenty-two.'

'Well, I can't stop you can I? You little bitch.'

I did not answer. I was hurt. Again.

At that time, he gave me driving lessons, he was impatient and angry with me and pulled the handbrake while I was driving. I asked him 'Please don't do that'

This resulted in him shouting 'You're a son of a bitch' while jumping out of the car I was practising in and slamming the door. He got into his car, slammed that door and sped off up the road.

I stood there in tears of anger and upset. I decided I would never get into any car with him again if I could manage it.

He used to text me when shows were on such as *Worlds' Worst Drivers*. Despite him using the 'bitch' term on previous occasions, when he said it about my decision to go to London it hurt me again.

I learned I did not feel the emotional abuse less just because it happened more. It was actually the opposite. I just gave up trying to challenge it because he chipped at me and wore me down slowly.

The further away from him I was, the happier I was. For my first few weeks in London, Mam and Paula called me every night, crying and telling me they missed me. I missed them too, despite that, it was fun for a while.

I partied with the English friends I knew from the trip to Australia. Although they were great fun and showed me around, I found it less friendly than Dublin. I missed the park and the sea.

I used to go straight to the seafront on every visit home. I needed my sea breeze sanctuary fix. After ten months of going home every second weekend to go out with Paula and my Irish friends I returned to Ireland homesick.

I was back in Mam and Dad's again. There was a brief interlude of him and me getting on before it returned to us not getting on.

After a trivial disagreement one morning he advised me in no uncertain terms: 'If you don't get out, I'll throw you out.'

I was alarmed by this because I did not know what I had done to annoy him so much and warrant that reaction. I knew it was not an idol threat. I had seen him take Shane's front door key from him.

I moved into a big old Georgian house in the heart of Rathmines in South Dublin with Sissy and three other girls. She was her super sassy self and some of her confidence rubbed off on me.

Shane and Sissy became good friends while I was away in Australia, playing pool and going to gigs together. The age gap of six years seemed less now between Shane and me.

One of his good friends was neighbours with us in Rathmines and we shared some of the same party scene. Paula asked to move in with me in Rathmines and it was comforting to have her there. She brought a calmer, more feminine and gentler energy to the party house.

Shane was staying in his friend's house around the corner and painting his back-garden wall for him while he was away. I ended up doing most of it while we sipped wine in the sun.

Shane liked writing and did a lot of that while I painted. He repaid my efforts in exchange for an old green mountain bike. I loved it and cycled up the road to work.

I was back working in the same organisation as a social care worker with children with autism. I loved it. I worked hard during the week and partied hard at the weekends.

After a couple of years like that and living in the house with the girls, Sissy and I decided to go to Thailand. I was excited to go back. I felt I was a bit stifled by Paula's conservative friends on the first trip there.

We had a party the night before we left. Dan, Shane and Paula were there too. Kerry was at home with her small children. Paula headed off to bed at 1am and Dan went on home because he had a match the next morning.

I decided to locate Shane. Normally he would be dancing around resembling some freed bird. I found him on his own lying on the old spare mattress on the floor in my room. It was there for my English friend who was staying over.

'Are you ok in here, Shane?'

'I'm good, Lucy, I'll be out in a while. I'm just having a rest in here.'

His facial expression looked strained like he was trying to block out a bad thought as opposed to the noise.

My bedroom was on the ground floor right beside the main area of the party. Sissy was blasting out records on the decks. Shane was wide awake, and he did not seem himself.

It crossed my mind that it seemed as if he was almost hiding from the party, he was acting a little paranoid. In particular the movement of his eyes. They darted behind me every now and then.

It was like he was waiting to see something, or he could see something that was not there. I wondered did he not want to go home alone. My gut told me this was not a good sign,

Shane staying in there on his own. I brushed it off. I told myself I was overthinking things.

I went back to the party and he was gone when I returned in the early hours of the morning. He left a note saying he was gone back around to his friend's house.

When the party was over, except for a few bodies strewn asleep about the house, I confided in my friend that was staying, that I had a feeling Shane was mentally unwell. I found myself using the word schizophrenic, yet I had no idea where I was getting that from. I cried myself to sleep.

The next morning, I thought I probably got it all wrong in my drunken state. I popped around to him. We had a shot of wine and a chat over breakfast before I said farewell.

Sissy and I jetted off still tipsy, for six weeks of fun. We island hopped, seeing beautiful beaches. We snorkelled by daylight and we full moon partied by night. Any moon at all partied.

Pretty quickly Sissy started seeing a Thai guy and hanging around with his friends who ran a beach hut bar. They were massive weed smokers. She spent a lot of time smoking and smooching with him.

We stayed on that island for the remaining four weeks. I was into the activity side of things for daytime and the dancing by night. I found other travellers to drink Thai whiskey with. Once we had seen the sights, Sissy and I got into a routine of staying up late and getting up late.

On the last morning of the trip, I came around from a whiskey, Red Bull and rum-induced blackout to find I was dancing in the sea.

It is a bizarre experience to come around to a view that solely encompasses the sea stretching out to the horizon. I looked down, my legs were in the water up to my shins and I was dancing to some beat in my rolled-up jeans.

I turned around and traipsed back on to the beach. I proceeded to get a lift home barefoot on the back of a stranger's motorbike. As far I was concerned, I was having a blast.

I slept some of it off and got up to have a shower in my hut. I was in nervous energy mode, whereby I was extremely over-tired and at the same time kind of hyperactive.

My mind was racing from six weeks of debauchery and I was fairly shook. I was literally shaking. I needed sleep but I knew my racing thoughts and alcohol induced anxiety would not allow that to happen.

I had no idea what I had done or who I had been with towards the end of the night. Anxiety flooded my head. I knew a shower was one thing that helped clam me down when I was like that. First, I had to vomit.

3

While I was in the shower, I saw a foot-long multi-coloured lizard on the wall. I froze in panic whispering 'Fuck, Oh fuck.' After taking some deep breaths I turned off the shower. I crept out of the bathroom.

I am not sure if I was hallucinating with the DT's. I packed up and found Sissy to say farewell. She was stoned. I knew she was staying on with her new friend. We both had tears in our eyes because our Asian antics were coming to an end.

I arrived back in Bangkok for my flight. I was shaking, sweating, full of fear and nauseous. The hangover was well and truly kicking in.

At the ATM I discovered I was penniless. I was even more fearful and anxious now. I only had the small amount of cash I had on me to get through the day and to find a place to sleep. I asked myself, *how the hell you let this happen, Lucy?*

The accommodation I afforded was grim. It was the type of green-grey room that people are either killed in or kill themselves in. It was dark, dank and depressing.

I dropped my bags off and went straight back out into the light and the heat. After buying my Taxi-Bus ticket for the airport the next morning I was left with enough money for two meals: dinner and breakfast.

Instead, I used it for the cheapest beer available to calm my nerves. I do not even like beer. I half slept that night. I was outside the Taxi–Bus shop front first thing the next morning.

The bus driver appeared, he had a sweet face and looked fresh in his white shirt.

He took my Taxi- Bus ticket and pointed towards another guy with a yellow backpack walking ahead of me. I followed him and his yellow backpack for a couple of streets. Five minutes later he stopped at a bus stop. I asked him, 'Is this where the taxi is picking us up?'

He looked at me vacantly. I realised I was not meant to follow him at all. I tried to go back the way I came. I had no clue which direction that was. Streams of sweat rolled down my back under my t-shirt, behind my backpack. I was on the verge of tears. I did not have a penny to my name and the taxi to the airport was prepaid.

All I saw were throngs of people. I did not know if I was even rushing in the right direction. My face was red and sweating. Then, the angel in his crisp white shirt appeared and came towards me. The driver realised my mistake and came to find me. I wanted to hug him.

I thanked him and God all the way to the airport. I was full of fear. I checked my emails in the airport. There was one from Paula saying that Dad was going to collect me from the airport. My stomach churned.

I wrote back, instructing that she tell him 'no.' she replied that he was insisting 'yes.' I knew I would be even further into the DTs by the time I got to Dublin.

The first thing I saw as I left the arrivals gate was Dad and Paula. As he paid for the parking, I whispered to her that she knew I wanted a chance to get it together before I saw Dad.

I wanted to shout at him because yet again I had to put up with him overruling my wishes at twenty-six years of age.

She said, 'We're here because of Shane, Dad will explain properly in the car.' I instantly got an even stronger uneasy feeling in my stomach. That distracted me from my annoyance at Dad. I was glad to see Paula's face.

I sat in the back of the car with the pair of them in the front. Dad explained, glancing at me every now and then in the mirror, that Shane had been extremely unwell. He was in a severe depression, accompanied by paranoia and he was refusing to get professional help.

Shane no longer wanted to discuss it with any of the family. He believed they were involved in some sort of conspiracy. Dad thought he might listen to me. They were all very worried about him. Now I was too.

While in Thailand out of nowhere I had a dream. There was an empty wooden chair with a black cushion seat in the middle of a bathroom. It was tiled on the floor and on the walls, it was all white. It was how I imagined a psychiatric hospital bathroom to look.

There was nothing else in that room except the chair. It was a chair that was in Mam and Dad's house. I woke feeling alarmed because I somehow knew the chair symbolized that Shane had taken his own life by hanging himself.

Deep down I think I knew he needed psychiatric help. I consoled myself by thinking it was too much alcohol giving me crazy dreams.

I wanted to see Shane with such a sense of urgency. I was silent for the trip, willing us all the way to get there quicker. I arrived at the house and said a brief hello to Kerry and Mam. They were sitting either side of Shane at the dining table.

They left us and I put my arm around Shane and asked him what was wrong. He described a vicious circle he believed he was in emotionally. It made sense and sounded very painful.

My heart hurt to see my beautiful brother this way. I made sure not to show it. I did not want to do anything to risk breaking his trust.

I was not a fan of medication, labels or hospitals. But it was clear he needed some professional support. He seemed broken.

I asked him if he would consider getting some help. I suggested perhaps the medically trained staff might have the experience to help him at the hospital to break the vicious circle he felt he was in. To my surprise he said that it might help him, and he agreed to go to the psychiatric services.

That night my parents took him to the local Accident and Emergency department. Due to red tape and politics over which catchment area he was to be admitted to, they had to drive around to three different hospitals. Shane became upset and distressed.

Eventually he was admitted into a psychiatric hospital in the countryside, miles away from our family home. The same one he had been in twelve years earlier.

This time around I was allowed to visit. I made sure of that. During the weeks he was there, the family and his friends went to see him regularly.

It made my heart heavy he had to be there. It did not seem right for him. When I visited him, once inside the metal doors clanged and locked behind me automatically. I wondered if he felt trapped, a caged bird.

I always entered slightly unsettled until I located Shane. I remember on one of the visits before he noticed me, I had a chance to observe him. He was sitting alone in a large communal area. His long gangly legs were casually crossed, and he had a book in his hand, looking like his normal self.

The chair was a tapestry high-backed chair. I had only ever seen these in a home for older people. It was not befitting a thirty-two-year-old, not my worldly Shane. I took a deep breath and attempted to put a smile on my face.

His green eyes met me with affection. 'Oh, hi Lucy. Nice jacket, turquoise.'

I gave him a hug and proceeded to rattle on all about an interview I'd come from.

'I thought they might appreciate the cord turquoise blazer, you know?'

He smiled at me. 'For sure, little sis.' As usual he was trying to make me feel good and succeeding. I wanted to do more for him.

'How are you doing in here, Shane? It's so old and stuffy?'

'I don't mind it. Dad offered to move me to the posh hospital in Dublin, but I'm ok here. The grounds are lovely, there is a beach not far either.'

I suggested, 'How about a walk?'

'I'm not allowed out without a staff member.'

'Oh, ok.'

I tried to sound casual and to act as if this was not so strange. That his new normal was fine. I went to the bathroom and on the way, I slipped over to the nurse's station.

'Hi, I'm Shane's sister, Lucy; I'm wondering can we pop out for a walk?'

'No, there is not enough staff, and he currently cannot go out unaccompanied.' The nurse sighed.

'Oh, ok then.'

I was afraid to ask why he had to be with a staff member. He seemed fine to me.

I left that evening with a lump in my throat and with a request from Shane for my parents. He wanted them to bring a pencil on their next visit. He loved to write and sketch. The simplicity of this request broke my heart.

Two nights later I got a panicked call from my parents' landline. It was Paula, crying.

'Shane got out of the hospital on his own.'

'What?'

'Yeah, Lucy, he was reported to Mam and Dad as missing from the hospital. I'm going with Kerry and two of Shane's friends to the hospital grounds to look for him now.'

'Ok, Paula.'

'Mam and Dad want you to come here in case he comes home, ok?'

'Ok, tell them I'm on the way.'

I hung up and ran around to the taxi rank.

As I arrived to the house, I could see Mam was waiting at the front door.

'Hi Lucy, will you go upstairs and watch out our bedroom window in case he arrives at the back of the house?'

I croaked with a lump in my throat.

'Sure, Mam.'

I ran up the stairs. I spent an hour looking out the back window. For some reason I also thought he might arrive that way. I stared at the garden and onto the lane behind it, but he did not appear.

There was no word from Paula and Kerry for a couple of hours, it was nearly 10.30pm. I called the police to report Shane went missing from the hospital at 8pm.

The policeman casually informed me Shane was reported missing at 6pm by the hospital staff. They did not tell my parents until 8pm. They had waited two hours to tell us. If we knew sooner, we would have been down there searching before it got pitch dark.

I described Shane to the policeman. 'He's tall and slim with brown hair and green eyes and he's wearing blue pyjamas.'

The policeman asked me to hold for a minute. I heard what he was relaying to his colleagues, 'Lads, some fella is gone missing; he has blue eyes and is wearing green pyjamas.'

When he got back on the phone, I told him that was the wrong description he was sending out. I repeated the correct description.

He replied with, 'Oh right, sure it's dark out anyway.'

I shouted at him, 'He is not some fella. His name is Shane, and he is my brother. A person. Not a fucking dog.'

I was fuming and terrified for Shane. I had to hide my tears from my parents.

I called the hospital next. They confirmed it was 6pm when Shane left. Someone left a large window open. I knew the ones, along the old corridors with huge discoloured anti-quated metal frames.

It was now 11pm. Shane was outside the hospital, alone, on an October night. We feared if he was unwell, he might stay out and freeze.

41

I knew we all had another huge fear that we were not mentioning what if he decided to take his own life. He was in a psychiatric hospital. He was not well.

I tried not to think of the dream I had in Thailand, the chair in the empty bathroom in the psychiatric hospital. It kept playing before my eyes.

My anxiety was increasing. I believed Shane knew he was not well, that must have been awful for him. I was sure he knew it was possible to get better. I prayed he had not lost hope.

Hours later, Kerry and Paula returned looking exhausted with pale complexions. The rest of the search party seemed defeated. There was no sign of Shane. They had searched the dark woods, a wild freezing beach, and the grounds of the hospital. We were all relived he had not been found dead, but we were worried as to where he was.

In the early hours of the morning Mam and Dad got a call to say he had returned to the hospital himself. He was unharmed and told the nurse he had been to the beach.

I admired his spirit. I did not blame him for wanting to get out. Going to the beach in the freezing cold in his pyjamas seemed extreme.

Mam and Dad drove straight to the hospital to see him. They arrived to find him on a skimpy mattress on the floor. He was heavily sedated. It seemed like beautiful Shane was being punished for wanting fresh air.

I asked my parents to take the hospital staff to task and they agreed. There were a lot of small things that did not seem right. We had a list of nineteen complaints, we decided to wait until Shane was discharged.

The next time I saw Shane he was in my parents' house. He was having a cup of tea on release from the hospital for the weekend.

I figured he did not know the whole family knew he had a trip to the beach. He appeared to be getting better slowly. His eyes looked less strained, and he appeared relaxed. He was now coming home for full weekends to stay with Mam and Dad.

After ten weeks Shane was discharged. He had a bedsit of his own but when he left the hospital he went to stay with my parents. I called over to him there a fair bit. He seemed to be doing well and to be in good spirits.

We chatted and watched films. When it was my turn to pick the DVD, we watched *Girl with a Pearl Earring* and ate orange cheese Doritos. We sipped red wine with a big fire burning and laughed that Shane was never too macho for a good chick flick. He was such wonderful company.

A couple of weeks later I was in my parents' house again and Shane was there too. I was out the back smoking a cigarette. I had been away at a Jazz Festival all weekend and the familiar hangover fear accompanied me.

He came outside to me and instead of joining me in a smoke, the way he normally would, he asked me to come back inside. He said he had news for me.

I came inside; he was sitting on the rocking chair in the sitting room. My parents were sitting on the couch.

He told me that he secured a job for himself in a horticultural centre. He said how much he was looking forward to starting work again in a couple of weeks. I told him how he deserved all good things.

I was relieved for him; he was getting back to his old self again. Yet there was something in his demeanour that made me uneasy. It was not like him to share news in this way. He was almost making an announcement. It was like he wanted to make sure it was known and in the company of my parents. I brushed off the gut feeling.

I was busy working away in the centre. The Thailand trip was long forgotten. I was still living with Sissy in the party house and every weekend we found an excuse to have one.

On a Saturday morning, the week following the Jazz Festival, I was just out of the shower, pickled in cider and shots from the night before with the usual anxiety that accompanied the hangovers. I got a call from my parents' house. It was Paula on the call.

'Lucy, you need to come to Mam and Dad's house quickly.'

I was scared and did not know what to think. 'What's going on Paula? Is it Shane?'

Paula would not tell me. 'I can't get into it on the phone, hurry up, and please just come on.'

'Ok, I'll jump in a taxi now.'

I tied up my hair in a messy pile on top of my head. It was soaking wet and not even brushed yet. As I put on my coat Sissy appeared.

'What's going on?'

'I don't know. I've to get to my Mam's quick.'

'Do you want me to come with you?'

'No, it's ok, thanks. I'll call you later when I know what is happening.'

I knew how private my parents were. Whatever it was they

44

probably would not want anyone outside of the immediate family to know.

I ran around to the taxi rank and jumped into a car. My mobile was nearly dead. The taxi man was kind; he offered to charge it, saying if it was an emergency, I might need it later. I hoped he was wrong.

I arrived at my parents' house and opened the front door with my own key. Dad must have heard me. He was standing at the end of the hall. He averted his gaze from mine. He was looking at the floor and it seemed he was gasping for breath. He nodded towards the sitting room.

Then he walked by me, shaking his head from side to side in a distressed way. He seemed to be crying and unable to make eye contact. I had never seen him cry before.

I went into the sitting room with my heart in my mouth. Mam was sitting down. Paula and Kerry were standing. Mam told me to sit down. I did as I was told, and I sat on the couch beside her.

I was afraid of what I was going to hear. At the same time my eyes were searching her face to see what I might find out.

Then Mam spoke: 'Shane hanged himself upstairs.'

My body involuntarily collapsed forward, folding in half, unable to take in what I was hearing.

Panic-stricken, I asked, 'Where is he now? Where is he now? Where is Shane now? Is he ok?'

Mam said, 'He was taken to hospital, your Daddy and me found him. The ambulance men took him to hospital.'

'Then why are we all here?' I asked, not realizing they had been waiting for me to get there.

Kerry, Paula and I sat in the back of the car with Mam and

Dad in the front while we made the silent journey to the local hospital.

Upon arrival we were directed straight into the Accident and Emergency department. As we followed the male nurse, I frantically looked in all the beds for my beloved brother Shane. I was sure I was about to see him. But when I did not find him, I realized we were being led out the other side.

We were going *via* the Accident and Emergency to another area. As we all piled in behind the nurse, I saw we had been taken into a small room. I thought, *oh God no, this is like those horrible scenes from a film where they take the family into to a small room to give them bad news.*

Kerry's husband was now there too. We squashed into the tiny space with two chairs. Mam and Dad sat down, the rest of us were standing. Then swiftly and unceremoniously the nurse announced, 'I'm sorry. Shane was dead when he arrived.'

I heard nothing else. Not one word. We may as well have all been suddenly plunged underwater. Yet I saw everything clearly. It all went into slow motion. Paula in her black coat with the big fur collar, collapsed. She fell back onto a radiator and slid onto the floor.

Mam and Dad clutched onto each other. My brother-in-law embraced Kerry and looked at me over her shoulder with an expression of disbelief.

This was beyond comprehension. It was as if I had fallen off a cliff into very deep water. I was drowning while having an out-of-body experience. I was in extreme pain, screaming on the inside yet simultaneously numbed and dumbfounded into silence externally.

I found myself outside the hospital building. I am not sure how I got there. I was too astounded to comprehend what just happened.

I lit a cigarette and called Sissy to tell her what happened. I think I was fairly matter-of-fact. She told me she loved me. I hated crushing her with this desperate news of her own friend Shane.

I went back in, another nurse asked for one of us to identify Shane's body with Dad. I went with her and him into an empty ward except for a few trainee nurses standing in a huddle at the far end of the room.

There he was. My beautiful brother Shane. He was lying on a grey trolley. There was no sheet and no pillow under his head. It looked like he was on a slab. I hugged his face. It was warm. He seemed alive, not dead, not Shane.

I kept saying, 'I'm sorry. We loved you. We loved you, Shane. We loved you. I'm sorry, Shane, we loved you.'

I looked up and caught eyes with a trainee nurse who was standing observing me. I looked at her and her at me; there were no words appropriate for the worst moment of my life.

A short while later I was nominated to call Dan and tell him our big brother had died. When he answered the call, I seemed to have another out-of-body experience.

I was watching myself alone again, standing outside the hospital on the phone saying to Dan 'It's Shane. He is dead."

He said, in almost a whisper, 'Ok, ok, how?'

'Dan, he did it in Mam and Dad's...' My voice was cracking under the strain of holding back the tears.

'Oh God.' He did not say or ask me anything else; he was able to tell it was suicide. I told him, 'Dad is coming to collect you.'

'Ok, Lucy.'

It was such a short call. There were no other relevant words just then for this tragedy. Nothing else was required to impart he had decided to carry out his ultimate and final irreversible act.

I regretted being the one to tear Dan's world apart. His life as he had known it would never be the same again. That broke my heart further.

We waited around for a while, before we were all brought up together to see Shane. Now he was on a bed in a single room instead of a ward.

He was lying on a lemon sheet and his head was on a pale lemon pillow. There was a tiny white flower with the tiniest bit of pink in the centre on the pillow beside his head, just beside his cheek. Somehow the flower crushed me even further.

Was this tiny thing of beauty an attempt to cheer us up? It was almost apologetic. Sorry, here is your dead loved one. We know he is gone suddenly and too soon. This tiny, beautiful flower might ease the pain of this tragic sight you see before you.

I found this as fucked up as my brother lying lifeless before us. It was too much, too sad, too painful and too cruel.

We went back to my parents' house that evening. We sat by the fire drinking tea and waited for Dad and Dan to arrive back. Mam met them at the door.

Dan was crying, 'He could have been stronger. He could have been stronger.'

We all sat together. It is hard to remember who said what. I do remember the relief when Dan stopped crying that night. There was something too sad about him, my little brother wailing big gulping tears. I wanted to take away his pain.

Later I returned to Rathmines with a bottle of red wine. I do not remember how I got there or where I got the wine. Sissy was there, waiting. She was crying too.

I put on Leonard Cohen's song *Suzanne,* Shane had introduced me to his music and so much more. I sat on my bed and cried and cried until I fell asleep exhausted.

4

I woke the next morning. The pain was not in my consciousness for a moment. Then it came: a severe punch to the stomach and heart, the memory of what had happened. My whole body ached. I was beaten physically and emotionally.

I got up in a haze and cried my way through a shower. My eyes burned as I cried relentlessly. I threw on the first thing I found and went back to my parents' house.

I had an aversion to wearing the khaki green coat I had loved. It was now the coat I found out Shane died in, never to be worn again. It had enveloped and absorbed all the shock and dismay and now symbolized that for me.

I went silently in the back of a taxi to avoid any small talk. When I arrived, there was no one there. The house was too silent. There was a note on the table from Mam saying they were at the funeral home. I was paralyzed on the spot.

I rang Sissy. I had to speak to her to be able to move while I left the house again. The notion of passing through the hallway knowing the landing above was the scene of Shane's devastating departure was horrific. It was like returning to a traumatic crime scene.

I got out as fast as possible and I walked up to the funeral home with tears rolling down my cheeks. Shane looked lovely. Dan and Dad picked a red and black check shirt for him to be buried in. He was wearing the new trousers and shoes he bought for the job. He told us all he was starting on the Monday.

It did not make sense; it was too hard to fathom he was actually dead. He went from being so alive and well physically. There was no period of decline. For him to now be gone was too much of a shock to get my mind and heart around.

I wondered if Shane intended to start the job or if the new clothes were part of a ploy. Either way I understood why he left. I knew he had been in pain. My heart was broken, and I already missed him dreadfully.

I did not want to ever forget him, so I asked the funeral home staff for a lock of his hair. Mam wanted one too, so they gave us a piece of his lovely hair. The same hair I helped him cut the dreadlocks out of years before. The same hair that caused so many arguments with Dad.

I cried as I looked at his hair and his face. He was a beautiful man inside and out. I asked myself *how Shane could leave us all when we loved him so much.* I thought I knew why.

He had been ill emotionally and left a note saying he did not want to live that way. I understood that. I even accepted it, I did. But I did not want to have to live without him. I did not understand how he thought any of us could or would ever want to live without him.

The next three days were a blur in my parents' house trying to help the family and our local priest with funeral arrangements.

At one point I said hello to an old friend who I had grown up with. He was in the sitting room; he informed me he had been there for the previous three days. I apologized. I had not noticed or seen him. I did not know what was going on around me. My mind was reeling.

We had to wait a week before having the funeral as there had to be an autopsy. I spent my nights in Rathmines and turned up each day at my parent's house.

I volunteered to keep the tea, coffee, biscuits and sandwich supplies stocked up. While I was in the supermarket, there was an announcement over the intercom. I wondered if Shane was schizophrenic and hearing voices if stuff like that freaked him out. *Did he know what a real voice was or not?* I was devastated thinking he went through all that alone.

I arrived back from the supermarket at my parents' house. Paula and Mam looked even more sombre than normal. Mam said she had received a call from the hospital.

'They have taken an organ belonging to Shane for research.'

I asked Mam, 'What organ did they take? His heart?'

She shook her head no.

'What then? They hardly wanted his lungs?'

'No, Lucy. They took his brain.'

I felt ill. My body went cold, and my mind was spinning. *How did they take his brain? They would have to open his head, but how? And where? Oh God no. Poor Shane.*

I was utterly horrified and devastated. It seemed barbaric to do that to any person and to someone I knew and loved. I said nothing and hugged Mam. I may as well have been hugging a sack of spuds. There was no hug back.

I remember during that time Dan crying saying, 'Mam did not even give me a hug when Shane died.''

I tried to console him, by telling him, 'me neither. Sure, she never does Dan.'

Not even now. She did not feel the need to care for us with a hug or a kind word of reassurance.

I was angry at the hospital staff. I wished they had asked our permission at the hospital or told us in person this was going to happen and not on a phone call. Greater respect from them for the family of the deceased should have been shown.

Once again there was no changing the situation, we found ourselves in. We had the funeral to arrange. I went into the kitchen to make a pot of tea to try to soothe us.

I heard banging and looked out to the back garden. There was Dad hacking apart a brown wooden chair with a black cushion on it. He was attacking it with an axe. I knew it must have been the chair Shane used. The same chair I saw in my dream.

I stood frozen and silent below the clock in the kitchen. There was no tick tock to be heard. It still said 2.30pm. Shane was alone in the house when he died. When Mam and Dad found him all the clocks had stopped in the house at 2.30pm. God bless our lovely Shane.

On the evening before the funeral the priest was in the house helping us to plan Shane's farewell. We wanted to make it a celebration of the good life he lived.

Whenever Dan or I spoke the priest kept saying 'well done' in a drawn out and exaggerated manner. It was non-stop. For some reason this cracked Dan and me up. After yet another 'Well doneeeee, Daanny.'

I had to cover my face and leave the room as if I was crying in an attempt to stifle the giggles. Dan was trying hard not to laugh too. Despite knowing it was wrong it was impossible not to laugh.

The day of the removal arrived, and we returned to the funeral home. We put a rolled-up cigarette in Shane's shirt pocket. He was forever smoking rolled up cigarettes 'rollies' and drinking tea. We would all miss those cups of tea and chats with him so much.

My rumination was interrupted because Paula was suddenly on the floor under the coffin. She had managed to kick over her whole cup of tea. It spilled on the cream carpet under his coffin. She was frantically trying to clean it up. We caught eyes and stifled our laughs.

Moments later they were closing his coffin. Mam, who was almost mute since she found him on the landing, shouted out, 'Don't go.'

It broke my heart into smaller pieces. It was so sad. Her beautiful boy, gone so soon. The rollercoaster of emotions was overwhelming. I alternated between bawling crying and being numbed by shock and disbelief.

When the removal was over that evening, we all got a Chinese takeaway in my parent's house. Sissy was with us and mentioned her time with Shane when I was in Australia.

'He played Mexican music while we ate our Mexican takeaway. He was gas. Jesus Christ, Lucy, I will miss him so much.'

They had been close. I was so wrapped up in my own grief it hit me how much all his friends including Sissy were hurting too. I squeezed her hand. 'You always made him laugh so much. He got such a kick out of you, he loved you to bits.'

She wiped her tears and then laughed wiping snots from her face. 'That means a lot. I loved him to bits too.'

I think she was in a little in love with him. I did not ask. It did not matter, romantic love, friendship love, sisterly love, we all loved him. I smiled at her to try to make her feel better.

We were all huddled around eating and it seemed weird, because it was. I felt guilty for having my chicken curry in the presence of his photo and a candle in the middle of the table.

As we sat in silence Paula dipped a chip in her curry sauce and offered it to Shane in the photo. We laughed and cried our way through that meal, grateful for Paula's dark humour.

After dinner Kerry disappeared. I found her lying on her bed in our old bedroom. She looked sad and almost vulnerable compared to her usual vivacious self.

While she was lying there, she told me, 'This morning my neighbour was washing her windows. I wanted to shout at them. How can you be preoccupied by something as bloody mundane when my world was just ripped apart?'

'It's so surreal. It's so hard to believe. It's the type of thing that happens in other families, not ours.'

I tried not to cry, not only for Shane or Kerry, but for our whole family. We were all torn apart with grief. This was how it was. Lots of crying interjected by attempts from us to diffuse the intensity with some laughter.

Although no one laughed as we followed the hearse in a limousine by our home. Shane was driven in his coffin by where he grew up and died. No one laughed at the church either. The reality we all desperately wanted to be untrue was too stark.

The hearse arrived outside the church. They opened up the back and the coffin was visible. My beautiful four-year-old nephew went over and put his hand on it. He was crying inconsolably. It was almost unbearable.

He seemed so tiny, but it was as if he understood it was his chance to say goodbye, better than I did at the time. It was like I was watching a tragic scene in a film instead of being at my own brother's funeral.

The ceremony for him was special. We played 'Starry Starry Night' by Don McLean and all I could do was try to keep myself upright.

Shane had a huge circle of lifelong friends. They were all at the funeral. Lots of long hair, leather, and parker jackets and wool hats. A clever beautiful bunch of people. One of them carried a tiny blue bike up to the altar to represent Shane's love of cycling. I put a Bob Dylan album on his coffin. I also wore the bright turquoise jacket he had admired on me at the hospital.

Despite the tragic circumstances of his death, I wanted to try to celebrate his life. I bought a new white fluffy jumper to wear too. I thought it was a strange thing to buy something new to wear for a funeral. It almost seemed vain, but I refused to wear black. I did not care what anyone else thought of my outfit choice. I knew Shane would appreciate my efforts for him.

On the PLC course they taught us about how various cultures mourn. I remembered having a conversation with Shane about an exhibition I had been to. 'Did you know, Shane that in Mexico they wear super colourful clothes at funerals? It's like a massive party.'

'Yeah, jeez, you know what? I think they have it right, Lucy. They celebrate the person's life. I'd way prefer that to all the morose songs sung so maudlin into pints of Guinness.'

He smiled.

'Yeah, me too, it's so morose. I love how in Africa they dance for days; I want people to celebrate at mine too.' I knew he was non-religious, non-conventional, and very non-judgmental.

Dan wore a black suit; I had never seen him in one. He was trying to be respectful and reminded me of the Tin Man. It appeared as if he could not bend his elbows and knees properly in it.

He also looked slightly choked by his tie. The weight that was put on him to be the one to say the final words about Shane in the church was evident in his pale face. He was taking sharp breathes, almost as if he was about to start hyperventilating.

As he went up onto the altar to read the eulogy, I could see Paula trying to brush the white fluff from my jumper off the whole side of his suit. I had been sitting right beside him during the ceremony. I suddenly felt worried. He gave me a look that told me not to worry. Dan has a good heart; all of my siblings do.

We all cried as we followed Shane's coffin out of the church. Mam chose to play Bob Dylan's song 'Blowin' in the Wind'.

How many roads must a man walk down before you call him a man? How many years can some people exist, before they're allowed to be free? How many times can a man turn his head and pretend he just doesn't see? How many deaths will it take 'til he knows that too many people have died? The answer my friend is blowin' in the wind.

My friends greeted me outside the church. I tried to joke

that I was finding kitchen paper the most absorbent for the floods. It was true and in private I was using towels to catch the tsunami waves.

We went to a local pub and everyone spoke of how special Shane was. It was weirdly uncomfortable talking about him in the past tense and being the 'bereaved.' Especially because he died by suicide.

People do not always know what to say. Back then death by suicide was not as common an occurrence. I heard the occasional sideways comment or whispered out of the corner of mouths, 'You know he did it in his mam's? Poor woman,' or, 'Apparently he was schizophrenic.'

Later tongues got looser. An old friend of the family told me 'I think he was selfish to do it. I don't blame you if you are angry.'

It hurt me to hear this. I tried to set him straight. 'I think he thought he was doing us a favour; he must have been in such a bad place to think that.'

'Yeah, well, I still think it was selfish.'

I was starting to get annoyed.

'Look, I cannot be angry at him for not loving himself. It's too sad.'

Once he realized I was not angry at Shane he muttered something and shuffled off. As he did, I contemplated going after him and shouting at him.

What the fuck do you know about him? His life? Why he died? Or how he died? Quit being so God damn judgmental.

Just then my Aunty Clare was shushing everyone, her husband was about to give a performance. My uncle Brendan started to sing The Clancy Brothers song 'Parting Glass', unaccompanied.

It was reminiscent of a tragic scene from an Irish film. It seemed so maudlin, so morose. It was well intentioned and heartfelt, but it made me want to run out of the pub.

When Aunty Clare joined in for the chorus tears rolled off my chin. All I could think was *surely this is the type of thing that happens to other families; not mine. How could someone so loved take their own life?*

I questioned myself *did he know how much I loved him? Did I tell him the last time I saw him, how much I loved him?*

I was not sure because I had been hungover after The Jazz Festival. I knew we never had a cross word, not ever, that was a comfort. The recent film we had watched together, every last detail of that night and the previous times I saw him all became so important now.

Shane teased me all the way home that he was going to have to endure my choice of DVD that day. I knew he did not mind, he was a soft soul. I wished I could have known it would be our last film together or what he was planning.

I always think of him now if I hear of that film or see those cheese Doritos. The thoughts of not sharing a meal, a cup of tea, a film, new music or books with him ever again seems so unfair.

I did not know what I was going to do without my protector and teacher. I thought he deserved to live longer.

One of Shane's friends jolted me from my silent reminiscing and cheered me up momentarily. Shane had confided in him.

'You know the night Shane went to the beach?' He asked me.

'Yeah, you all went down looking for him?'

'Well, yeah, Shane told me he was invited into a little caravan by an old guy living in it. They sat together chatting and drinking whiskey.'

'No way.'

It was a small comfort to me to know he had not been alone that night. He was enjoying a drink.

'I'm proud of him for giving the hospital the two fingers.'

'Me too, Lucy. He left that hospital. He wanted to get out for a walk, so he went to the beach, good for him.'

I nodded in agreement with a half-smile on my face.

Yet saddened this was how Shane lived in his final months.

I do not remember the end of the night of the funeral. I can only gather I was drunk.

The following week was spent in my room listening to music, crying my eyes out. I went through all my photo albums and found every photo of Shane. I did not want to forget a thing about him or our times together.

One week later I returned to work. I tried to smile but it was impossible. I spent my days in a stupor, doing my best and often failing to keep the flood gates closed. My friends at work were incredibly kind and understanding and so was Sissy.

Weeks after the funeral, Mam got a call to say Shane's organ was released for collection. The whole family went together to collect it.

Mam carried the tiny wooden box. It was smaller than a shoe box. She carried it out of the morgue to my parents' car the way a person carries a box with an injured bird inside. She was wearing the same clothes she had on for the funeral, and she was sobbing. Her whole body shook. Almost as if she might collapse.

Seeing my mother carrying my big brother's brain in a box is the most disturbing and saddest thing I have ever seen. All these years later I cannot catch my breath when I recall that image.

That afternoon was akin to a strange small funeral that only the immediate family knew of and attended with this miniature coffin type box. We had to bring his brain back to him and to bury it with him in his grave ourselves. The rest of the day is too much to bear remembering. It is too traumatic to think about it.

Many months of being in a haze of sadness went by. I cycled to and from work; my green bike gifted from Shane was going strong. Everything he ever gave me now became extra precious.

On my way home one evening as one of the service users passed by me, he waved enthusiastically from a car. I smiled and waved back at him.

I wondered about this unfamiliar feeling. I had accompanied the wave with a smile. I was happy at the service user's enthusiasm to see me.

Sissy was there when I arrived home. 'You know, I found myself smiling on my way home and I actually felt a bit guilty.'

'Ah, Lucy, Shane would want you to be happy. He would be happy that you're happy, if you know what I mean?'

We smiled at each-other. I knew what she meant. 'Yeah, I know he would want me to be ok.'

'We need to get out; you have been hiding away too much, it's not good for you.'

I launched into the family update 'It hasn't even occurred

to me to go anywhere other than work or my parents' house. Did I tell you they are having a crisis? They are wondering should they move out of the house. Mam wants to stay. She feels close to Shane there. Dad wants to leave.'

'Oh God, what do you think?'

'I don't know, I'm fairly numb, it's up to them. I can see why she wants to stay, and he wants to go. God. Come on let's not talk about this anymore.'

'Ok, let's go into town?'

'Yeah ok'

Sissy did a little hip wiggle, 'Whoo hoo, that's the Lucy I know and love.'

I was willing to do anything to fill the bottomless ache inside. We went to a usual haunt. Her boyfriend was the DJ there. Normally I would request songs and dance the night away. Instead, I did a lot of drinking and a lot of smoking.

I had plenty of years of practice of putting on a happy face when I was plastered. This time I had an overwhelming sense that was even stronger than guilt. It was akin to disgust at myself for being in a bar. It seemed too soon after Shane passing away and too disrespectful to him. It filled me with horrible feelings.

I stayed for a while and went home full of booze. I held back the tears until I was in bed. Then I cried myself to sleep. The hangover was horrendous, worse than normal. The anxiety and the tears caused me to feel almost suicidal myself.

I continued on mostly numb for the next three years except for the knots of anxiety in my stomach. Despite feeling like a mess, I got a call from the manager at work. She invited me for an interview for a senior post. The organization I was working for was expanding. I agreed to go.

I was sick with nerves. Shane's death had shaken the foundations of my being. Wearing makeup to conceal tired eyes, saying mantras and taking homeopathic remedies all helped me to keep things looking normal on the outside.

Cider helped too at the weekends. It was my scaffolding, a dodgy one at that. Another shake up and I might crumble.

I went along to the interview full of nerves. I answered 'no' to questions about experience I had obtained. I went blank giving examples. I did not get the job. I thought I was losing my interview charm as well as my confidence.

Once I was so convincing at an interview for a recruitment agency that they offered me a job in the agency. I even had the balls to take it despite only having half the required experience. After three weeks I made my excuses and ran back to social care.

Normally if I set my mind to something it happened. Paula used to say I had a genie in my pocket. Not anymore by the looks of things.

I sheepishly phoned the manager and asked for feedback on the interview. She explained they presumed I had a degree. It was not possible to offer me the role or the salary with the diploma qualification I had.

This gave me the kick in the rump I needed and off I trotted as a mature student aged twenty-nine to study for a Social Studies degree and a Social Work masters.

Paula advised me in a serious tone, 'Now, Lucy, you might not get into Trinity.'

'Paula, it's the one place that does five years in four, the placements are during the summer. It would be so handy.'

'I know, Lucy, just don't get your hopes up too much.'

'Look, you never know I *might* get in.'

I attended the mature student interview and told them how I wanted to work with people in recovery from addiction.

Then I did an academic written assessment. I was required to explain how I would support a lesbian couple, experiencing prejudice with their parenting. I must have done something right because I got accepted.

5

I spent the first year in huge lecture halls feeling like an intruder. I waited for a lecturer to come tapping me on my shoulder. I almost imagined I heard them. *Lucy, there has been a mistake here. Will you kindly leave please without making a fuss?*

While I waited for the results of my first set of exams, I prayed to Shane to let me have passed. I invited him to walk around the college with me. It was not as pretentious as some people tried to convince me it would be. Some of the students did love to debate obnoxiously. They were the minority.

I relished the feeling in the library among all the books. I sensed the history in the air. That was my favourite place in the college. I used to go up to the law students' section to soak up the atmosphere of hundreds of years of people studying those books.

My other mature student friends and I never tired of the novelty of the dining hall. It was vast with long wooden tables and huge portraits on every wall. It looked like Harry Potter's school.

When I was in school, I did not have aspirations to go to Trinity College. It was never even on my radar. Once I was studying there I fell in love with the place.

I skipped across the cobbles in heels and hats, a ball gown, and later, wearing a graduation cap. I believe Shane would have understood my appreciation of the old buildings and he would have been proud of me.

I still missed him so much and I envied Mam when she said she had an instant acceptance that he was gone, and she felt he was with her. I did not.

I went to plenty of churches. Everywhere I went I found one. There was a beautiful little church near the college off Grafton Street. It was ornate, with plush carpet and it was peaceful. But I did not find Shane there.

Occasionally I went to his grave, but I did not feel he was there either. Yet he must have been listening to my prayers. Despite being convinced I must have failed every single exam, I passed them all.

For the first time ever, I was at the top of my class. I realized I was not a 'thick' or a 'fool.' Dad had been wrong to imply that over the years. That realization spurred me on to give the course my all over the coming years. For the next three years I was either doing college work or I was working part-time in social care services.

I managed to wrangle one big night out a week with my new college pals. We hit up plenty of pubs. I discovered mojito cocktails and kissed some random stranger. I found that out via text from him the next day. I had no recollection. This was another drinking anxiety-inducing event.

I got to go on a J1 aged thirty-one to Boston for a summer. My friend and I did the law of attraction on it. I visualised what I wanted to happen. Then I behaved as if it was happening. I made our plane boarding passes and put them in our passports.

I did this in the hope we would be the two chosen from the class to go and we were. I loved Boston. As with every time I went away, I did not want to return. The fees to transfer to

66

college over there were thirty-three thousand dollars so I returned to Dublin again.

I began attending a Buddhist centre in Dublin weekly. There was a lovely atmosphere and a lovely bunch of people. I knew I had lost my faith or never really had a real one. I went there every week for one year to meditate in a group and learn about Buddhism. I was possibly trying to substitute faith with meditation. It slowed my mind down.

In my final year I was doing well in my assignments. Even with using spellcheck I mixed up my spellings. I knew how to spell but certain words I wrote them down wrong. I took a test online which showed I have mild dyslexia. That explained my life-long spelling struggles at last. I was relieved to know that.

I buried my head in the books, working, going to classes, and studying. I had to drop half of my shifts per month as the college workload was so heavy at the end.

I got through the weeks by budgeting. I had enough for porridge for breakfast, a cheese and olive sandwich for lunch, and frozen salmon with rice for dinner. This became my staple diet: healthy but lean. I knew it would not be forever.

Up until the final exams in fourth year I doubted myself that I was good enough. Despite successfully finishing, obtaining the degree and masters I was so nervous on the graduation day.

My legs wobbled as I went up to collect my master's certificate. There was a huge book to sign, one by one as we came back down. My hand shook so badly signing the book that my signature was illegible.

I was still happy and proud that my signature was in a book with all the people who have graduated from Trinity over the years. I thought that was cool.

We made arrangements to go out as a family for dinner that day. This was not a common occurrence for us. Dad always complained that there was too much garlic in everything, the music was too loud, or it was too expensive.

He refused to go to the same restaurant as my three closest college friends to celebrate that day. They were going to a fancy hotel off Grafton Street.

Dad told me, 'That's for movie stars. Don't get above your station. Find somewhere on the north side, that place on Henry Street.'

I was upset and disappointed. I was worried my friends felt a bit snubbed by me too. Instead, we had our meal in a restaurant in the north of the city.

Dad made it clear at the end of the meal that being partnered off was still the most important thing in his mind. He was drunk and offered the waiter money as a 'joke' to 'take her off my hands.' 'Her' being me, the new graduate. I was embarrassed and chalked it up as yet another hurtful moment from him.

Around that time, I unexpectedly got some tax back, so I booked a solo trip to Thailand for six weeks, for three weeks later. Paula lent me a big black backpack. I piled in seven books, knowing that was too many.

Dad heard I was planning on visiting hill tribes in the north of Thailand. He became very concerned. 'Do you know people can get eaten by the cannibals there?'

I stifled my laugh once I realized he was being serious. Despite being thirty-two and visiting Thailand twice before I had to quickly manifest a travel companion.

'Nah, it will be fine, really. I'm meeting my friend over there. We are going to a really touristy part.'

It was not worth telling him I was going alone. Dan joked that I should take a cardboard cut-out with me for the photos.

While I was packing, I came across the blue hat I bought at Blackrock market years before. Shane once had a record stall there. I had a lump in my throat thinking of when I dropped into his record stall on that day. I was sporting the new hat and he complimented me on it.

I wanted to tell him of the adventure I was going on. I chatted to him silently, but I did not feel him there.

Despite my promise to myself not to bring too much I filled my backpack to bulging including the hat and all the books. I planned to relax and read.

Paula dropped me to the airport. I was on a high, but she was so nervous for me that when I got on the first flight I was now worried too. My lack of a plan or a companion seemed to be a huge deal. I cried for hours on the first flight feeling panicked and upset.

I did not think through what I was going to do for six weeks in Asia alone. I was not mentally prepared at all. I was not even practically prepared. I had the first three nights booked and the rest was to unfold.

In the middle of an eight-hour panic attack the air steward arrived with my meal. I was all over the place. I put my meal tray down, but my seat was reclined.

He placed my cutlery in front of me and crouched down to his trolley to get my meal. I was trying to make space, so I picked up the knife and fork and put my tray back up.

I was trying to put my seat back up to the sitting position. I hurriedly pressed the button on the inside of the armrest with force to raise the back of my seat up. In the process I accidently managed to stab the fork into the air steward's arm. He let out a very loud screech. I instantly apologised. I was horrified.

Whenever he passed me, I sheepishly smiled at him while trying to look for a bloodstain on his shirt sleeve. I had to find a way to calm down. I knew I was acting crazy, even more crazy than normal.

I remembered I had some Eckhart Tolle, the mindfulness master, on my phone. During the next few hours, I played it over and over to block out all the fearful thoughts causing me anxiety. He was repeating, 'Just surrender, just surrender, just surrender.' Eventually I did and I started to breathe normally again. My mind and my heart rate slowed down.

I even had a nap and upon arrival I was my old self. I floated through Dubai airport to my next flight. Likely with the help of the red wine I had on the flight and Nina Simone's *I'm Feeling Good* in my ears. I was at one with the world again.

That was until I arrived in Bangkok. It was way too much of an attack on all of my senses. The smell of fried meat everywhere, the vast amount of people and the rubbish strewn around.

I found it too hot, hectic, and overwhelming. I stayed for one night and headed off on the bus trip for the hills and hammocks. I needed a reprieve from the hustle.

The bus climbed up the north of Thailand's steep terrain for hours and finally came around a corner. A spectacular view of miles of green lushness was revealed. It was completely unexpected and beautiful. Tears of relief overcame me. I was breathing easily again, and I knew I was somewhere very special.

After getting off the bus ride at a prearranged destination, I waited for an hour for my lift. It was getting dark, and I was eager to get to my hill tribe hut. My lift arrived and I found myself driving with a kind and mostly toothless guy.

He smelled of whiskey and I wondered how safe I was as we crawled up a practically vertical hill in his bandy four-by-four in the dark. The relief was immense when we arrived at the accommodation.

There was a very low-lit shelter with seating and tables underneath. He introduced me to the kind and gentle face of his wife. She showed me to a hut. It had no electricity. I knew this was the case in advance but somehow it seemed less of an exciting challenge now.

I smiled nervously as she closed the door and left me inside. I rummaged in my backpack and found my torch. It lit up a large space with a double bed and a mosquito net hanging over it. I took off my boots, unrolled my sleeping bag, and jumped in. I put on my phone, there was no signal, but my music worked. That comforted me to sleep.

I woke the next morning with something on top of me. The net had fallen down in the night. I crawled out from under the big net's web. My hat that I left under my pillow, to remind me Shane would mind me and my socks that I left beside my shoes were both way over the other side of the hut.

That was roughly six feet away. I wondered how on earth they got there. Unless an animal came in or I slept walked.

I soon forgot this unsolved mystery when I went outside. I saw I was staying in one of the four huts on the side of a mountain. One side of my hut encompassed the stunning view I had witnessed from the bus. I could see a woman working peacefully among rice paddy fields in the distance.

I had my own hammock. The bananas on the trees were within my reach. On the other side I saw the couple from the previous evening serving people breakfast. The shelter was also a restaurant. It was heaven on earth.

Over breakfast I met an older French lady, Sylvia, the most elegant older woman I ever met. She exuded calm. She was also travelling alone and staying in one of the other four huts. In comparison to her I felt girlish and a jittery one at that. I pretended hard not to be.

We had freshly made pancakes with bananas picked from the nearby trees and went trekking together. Sylvia and I agreed to have dinner together on Valentine's night. Neither of us wanted to be alone.

We ate fresh fish and fruits and shared stories of lost loves, the odd couple. She was a free spirit. I was trying to free my spirit maybe.

We visited the nearby hill tribe. They cooked us purple rice inside bamboo shoots on a fire inside of a hut. It was scrumptious. I was in awe of their beautiful way of life, living nestled in nature and their willingness to open their home to us. Even if the smoke choked us.

One week later I left the hills for the city of Chang Rai. I was unimpressed by the city compared to the sheer beauty of the northern hills. I was relived it was a smaller city and easier going than Bangkok. I wanted to hold on to the peace I had obtained up there in the hills.

I booked myself on a group trekking. They picked up the six of us going on the trek from the city and took us on an overnight trip. We trekked for eight hours and for some crazy reason I wore tight jeans.

I was probably thinking a snake would find it hard to get into them or bite through them. I am terrified of snakes. It was so hot, and my jeans were so heavy I thought I might die from spontaneous combustion.

We arrived at the overnight spot. I was beside myself with relief. I would not be able to go as far as to call it accommodation: it was bedding on a floor and a roof. We had a delicious meal sitting on the hills and a singsong before we retired to the large communal shack. We all slept side by side on the floor.

We trekked all the way back down. That was bearable on the legs. Everyone went their separate ways and agreed to meet that night for dinner in a bar. I was trying to stop drinking.

I was well aware now that once I started, I did not always stop. Either that or I did not remember the latter half of the evening. I told myself I was not going to drink that night.

Yet I drank that night with the tour group. I drank a lot, quickly and I got very drunk. The fear the next day was horrendous. I was lucky I did not lose my money or even worse my passport.

Over the years I lost so many mobile phones, jackets, cameras, bank cards, makeup, shoes, money, and bags. Any umbrella I ever brought out on a night out never returned with me.

I have vague recollections of three of the group walking me home. I was lucky in many ways to escape that situation unscathed. Anything could have happened to me.

I was shaky from drinking too much and I was delighted to meet up with the fabulous Sylvia again. She was in the city now too. We had dinner and a wine cure and swapped stories of our love lives. She likened our time together to a scene from a Woody Allen film. Everything seemed more exotic and interesting in her French-Canadian accent. She made the name of her lover Deter sound poetic.

It was great meeting people like her and seeing beautiful sights. Yet not the same as when I was there with Paula or Sissy. The cities looked greyer and dirtier. I was not sure if it was because they were sun-bleached and older. Or if it was because I was travelling alone, without any close friends who knew me. I wondered if it was because I was seven years older. Which was hardly a lifetime.

The last time I was there Shane had been alive. I was suddenly aware that there was the life I had before Shane died. That world had been mostly safe and happy and full of potential. I believed that amazing things were possible.

Then there was life after Shane died which felt very different. It did not feel as safe. Terrible things can happen, and they did.

No matter how hard I tried, it was hard for me to feel and experience the wonder around me. It was there before my eyes, but it was as if there was a grey mist between me and it. This bothered me. Misery followed me to Thailand.

I questioned myself if that was why I loved Boston so much. The American attitude of anything positive is possible helped to breathe life back into my heart and soul temporarily. I was properly alive again there. There were no Shane reminders or a previous trip to Boston to compare myself to my former happier self.

I felt a piece of me died with Shane. I was grieving for him and for my former self. I missed my confidante and my former confidence.

I heard a restaurant playing Bob Marley's song 'Three Little Birds' as I walked by: *Don't worry about a thing, cause every 'lil thing is gonna be alright.* I started to cry; it was too hard to listen to that song. I missed him too much. It reminded me of how much he cared for me and was there for me, from such a young age.

I tried to be there for him too over the last number of years. We enjoyed tea, smoked and chatted together. When Shane was not well, I encouraged him to talk to me. I would have done anything for him. I wished I had done more.

He probably tried to protect me even regarding his illness, maybe not telling me how bad it was for him. His departure was the biggest shock of my life and on top he was not there to make it better. It was like when you see a boxer getting a double punch one straight after the other. They become a bit dazed.

I could not believe he was gone. Here I was many years later still feeling dumbfounded. Maybe the shock had not worn off. Ever since he died there was an element of numbness for me at special occasions.

Even within the family I was a bit lost. He was the one I stood beside at all the occasions. I felt I was standing alone.

It was hard to get used to life without him and to accept that he was not sharing all the experiences with us all.

It was as if I was watching my own life through a fog. Some days it would clear more than others. I saw and felt everything: the good and the bad. The fog protected me from being overwhelmed by pain and sadness, but I was missing out on the joy to be had too.

Intellectually I knew deep down my life was good and it had potential to be great. I did not always feel that way. I wondered if this was more than grief. I wanted to be properly happy again. It was never so evident to me how much I had changed until the cities in Thailand looked jaded to me. I was too.

Four years studying and working full-time had taken its toll. The gloss from life seemed gone, it was all matt. I wanted to see and feel all the beauty again that I knew was around me. This new colour blindness was no fun.

Slowly over the weeks on my travels a sepia lens replaced the grey. I hoped it was leading the way back to the multi-colour I was once accustomed to. I promised myself if I got it back, I would never take it for granted again.

I decided perhaps it was time to try to say goodbye to Shane, to let him go. I did not want to. I had to try to let him go, for my own sake too. He would want that. I had to let myself be happy again.

I went back to my hut and sat outside that evening by the light of a candle, and I wrote him a letter. Twenty-six pages later I went to bed. I was twenty-six-years old when he died. Now I was thirty-two, the same age he was when he died. I heard before that things happen in seven-year cycles. I hoped it was the end of one cycle for me soon and the start of another.

The next day I felt nothing much after writing the letter to Shane. I made my way to a stunning small temple for some solace. Outside I saw a large stone bowl-type structure filled with water. There were four lotus flowers floating on top. I looked closely I saw there were five, one was under the water.

The lotus flower looked like a larger version of the tiny open flower that had been placed on the pillow by hospital staff beside Shane's face the day he died. I imagined that the flowers I was looking at represented the five children in my family. One was not visible, but it was there.

I found a closed lotus flower outside the temple; it was a brilliant green, the same as a new shoot of grass. I brought it inside with me. I was surrounded by stone and gold Buddha's. I spotted what looked similar to a fancy tabernacle box on a stand. It was glass with gold ornate decoration between the panes. The door was open, and it was empty.

There were some monks in their orange robes sitting on a huge stage. Children were sitting on the floor below and in front of them. They were learning and chanting with the monks. I stood to one side, watching.

The temple was beautiful with lots of gold intricate murals of figures feasting and dancing all over the walls. It was a lovely spot to try to say goodbye to Shane. I waited until they were finished. I quietly admired and photographed some of the murals.

Then I sat on the floor and took a photo of the closed lotus flower lying on the red carpet. It looked ready to open for a new life. The temple emptied out completely. I said some prayers and placed the lotus in the glass box. I knew it was not a tabernacle.

I was also praying to all kinds of various gods, angels and saints in a temple, which may be frowned upon. I reconciled myself that the various gods would understand. If I have an eclectic mix of religion surely, they would not mind. I figured covering all my bases was no harm. At this stage I needed all the divine intervention available.

After putting the lotus into the tabernacle type box, I sat on the red carpeted floor. There were incense sticks there to take and light off some candles. I sat there and watched it burn. I decided it was time to leave the temple. I saw a boat trip advertised on the way in. I planned to go on that for the afternoon.

I accidentally went out the back of the temple and found myself on a dirt road. I took a minute leaning on a white-washed house's window ledge to lap up the heat. The sun was bouncing off the white stone walls behind me.

I was in my own world, until I heard a car engine. I had not even noticed, I was standing closely parallel to a fairly old parked car with two people inside it. One person was in the driving seat and the other was in the passenger seat. They sat there for a minute before moving off.

It was then I noticed as the car slowly drove away from me a huge red sticker the whole size of the big back bumper saying 'HAPPY.'

I instantly thought it was a sign from Shane telling me he was happy. In my mind he was literally being driven off in the sun. I whispered goodbye to that car. I felt I knew what I had to do. I would treat the loss of Shane as if he were living abroad very happily. I could write or talk to him whenever I wanted even if it was not possible to see him.

I left feeling more content. On the boat trip we stopped at a waterfall and I swam in it for hours. I had never been in a waterfall before. I stood underneath letting everything wash away. I felt re-energized by the water splashing down on me and swirling in a powerful pool around my feet. I was on a natural high afterwards. I slept soundly that night.

The next day I tried white water rafting. I went on an organized tour. The water seemed clearer and crisper. People's expressions enticed me. I found myself screaming my head off with excitement and fear.

Laughing at myself by the campfire afterwards with my fellow rafters. None of them had let out any yelps. I did not care one bit. I was feeling and seeing everything clearer, and it was so refreshing.

Next, I got on an eleven hour overnight train all the way to South East Thailand. I thought it would be romantic, even though I was travelling alone.

Instead, I stood on a Thai wasp that severely stung me. So much so I let out a shout and some tears. A drunk German guy decided he would rescue me. He beat the wasp to death with his shoe in the confined carriage space.

I pulled the curtain around my bunk unnerved by the attention from this drunken wasp whacker. I wished I had my friends to share some of this experience with. We would have laughed. Instead, I ended up crying myself to sleep with the comfort of my music, listening to Simon and Garfunkel singing their song 'America'.

I wished I was on a trip with a lover too, people watching and pretending other passengers were spies, whose bowties were *really a camera*. I was homesick and a bit scared that night. That song brought me comfort many times on the trip.

It was a strange experience heading towards Koh Phangan, the full moon party island, without Paula or Sissy. I was going to the opposite side of the island to a place called The Sanctuary.

When I got off the train, I had a hair-raising motorbike ride up and down steep hills to the harbour area. Initially it was exciting and then it turned terrifying with the weight of my backpack feeling nearly as big as myself. I was convinced I was going to fly off and die.

I repeatedly shouted 'Fuck, fuck, fuuuuuck.' as we went down a steep hill at high speed. My driver seemed very entertained by this.

This turned out to be nothing compared to the boat trip that was to follow. I jumped off the bike at the beach. It was evening time, and I was the last traveller. A storm was coming.

Two guys took me across the short ride to the other side of the island in their battered boat. They seemed hesitant regarding if it was safe enough, but they decided to take me. The rickety boat swung so violently from side to side that I flew off my seat and landed on the floor beside my backpack. I saw the life jackets. They were two feet away, but I was too paralyzed with fear to get one.

That seems absurd but it was true. I was too terrified to move, speak or even breathe. I prayed to God, to Shane, to Buddha, to the angels and saints, and to anyone listening to please let me live. They listened.

We arrived and one of the guys plucked me off the floor. He cradled me like a baby while he waded through the water. He embedded me on the shore while the other followed and plonked my backpack beside me. As they disappeared, I trundled up the beach looking like a shaky baby turtle.

Never had I arrived at such an aptly named place. It was certainly a sanctuary for me after the train, bike, and boat rides. I embraced the peace of the place. It was a stunning location with white sand and turquoise warm water. I discovered big dunes to climb up that overlooked the sea views.

I enjoyed the super healthy food. On the first night I fell asleep on the beach at sunset to the most beautiful African flute player I will never forget. That was a magical moment. I tried everything that was on offer from transformational breathing workshops to meditation and massage.

I met other guests and by night I hung out with stoners who existed on shakes, pretentious poets and an angst-ridden American who pretended to be Canadian for fear of being judged. It was cool and cringe in equal measures.

After a few days I ran out of cash, all this wellness did not come cheap. I had to make the scary boat trip again to the other side of the island to an ATM. Luckily the waters were calm.

As we arrived, I was sickened by the state of the beach. There had been a full moon party the night before. There was rubbish everywhere. I got my money, and I went back to The Sanctuary on the next boat and stayed for the rest of the week. After sun gazing sunrises with stray dogs for company and stargazing nights with the stoners I moved on for Konchanaburi.

6

I missed my train by minutes. A tuk-tuk driver brought me to a local bus. No one on the bus spoke English and I did not have any Thai. I expected it to be a three-hour drive but three became four and four became five. Every now and then I stood up and asked, 'Can anyone please tell me where this bus is going?'

They smiled at me and looked at each other muttering in Thai what I imagined to be, 'Ah look at that poor eejit. What is she doing on this bus anyway?'

My blood pressure felt high. My cheeks were red from the stress of being afraid to stay on the bus and afraid to get off. I was relieved when an English-speaking French guy joined the bus. We arrived seven hours later.

After a couple of days of visiting the floating markets and pottering around exploring I was checking my emails in an internet shop. The same French guy appeared with his friends. They invited me to go for beers which resulted in us being ushered, in the early hours of the morning, from the lobby of my accommodation with our bottle of Thai whiskey.

The next morning the fear hit me with a bang. I felt nauseous. Anxiety filled every vein. Anything could have happened to me hanging out with random men. I had to travel to my next destination, back to Bangkok.

It was strangely a relief to be back in a familiar spot with lots of English-speaking people. Myself and another lonely traveller smoked cigarettes and drank beer to pass the hours before bedtime and flights.

I received an email to say the social work panel interview I attended before I left Ireland went well and there was a permanent children in care job awaiting me. I told myself it was *last chance saloon* that I should take it. This was without stopping to ask myself did I actually want to accept it.

I caught my flight back to Dublin minus any lost Taxi–Bus drama. I slept for most of the trip home. Despite being paranoid that they gave me a whole aisle to myself because of the steward fork-stabbing incident on the flight over.

When I returned, I found myself a beautiful bright one bedroom apartment on the coast in Dublin I set up all my paints and canvases. I cut back on drinking again, it scared me that despite trying not to drink I got blackout drunk in Asia.

I attended a counsellor for anxiety and the grief, and I mentioned it to her. She suggested I was 'allergic to alcohol.'

I suspected she was implying I was an alcoholic and I was appalled. 'I'm not an alcoholic, I drink on the weekends and on trips, the weekend is not even Thursday to Monday anymore. I have the occasional big blow out.'

She challenged me, 'Well if you are not an alcoholic then why don't you stop drinking for one year?'

I agreed 'Sure, that'll be easy enough, good idea, sure I'd be delighted to stop for a year.'

I told a friend of mine. He was the one person I knew of that went to addiction recovery meetings.

'Apparently I'm allergic to alcohol.'

He did not hold back. 'Lucy, you know she's trying to say you're an alcoholic, that's what that means.'

'Well, *you* know I'm not? I don't even drink every day.'

'Yeah, but I used to drink like you, binging and blacking out and I ended up an everyday drinker.'

He was back in his recovery meetings and admitted while we had been hanging out, he often had a bottle of vodka in his backpack, and he had to sip from it. I was worried he was trying to recruit me into the recovery meetings. I was starting to feel a bit panicked now and went quiet.

'Look, I'll get you a recovery meeting book and you can see what you think yourself.'

'Ok, thanks.' I sighed.

The following week he gave me the recovery meeting book. It was stories by alcoholics about their drinking and a description of the twelve steps programme. I read some of the stories. People were writing how they drank to give themselves confidence and to put on a smile when they wanted to cry. I identified with them. I felt sick with fear and shame. I asked myself, *I can hardly be an alcoholic, can I?*

I quickly jotted down the date on the book and I put the book away in an unused drawer. I was determined that I was going to stop drinking from that date for one year. I was going to prove I did not have a drink problem. I told myself I was not an alcoholic and wondered how he and the counsellor dared even suggest such a thing. I had a lovely home and a job, and I did not drink every day.

Dad and a lot of my aunties and uncles binge drank the way I did too. I thought this was normal. Alcoholics surely ended up on a park bench with twine holding their coat together, drinking from a brown paper bag. All my coats were intact.

The new social work job was in Dublin city and I was extremely busy. The weekends were filled with walking or cycling on the seafront. Within a couple of months, I was meeting up with friends for drinks again.

I forgot all about the existence of the book, the friend who told me about the recovery meetings, and the counsellor. As far as I was concerned, I was handling my drinking again. I ignored the fact that I was still having horrendous hangover anxiety that sometimes lasted days.

Paula was organising to move to America and got married first. At the wedding, Dan and I tore up the dance floor for hours. The happy couple asked me to collect all the cards from everyone, presumably filled with cash gifts. I dutifully did that, until I was drunk and abandoned the cards and other gifts in a corner.

Dan and his girlfriend stayed in my place that night. The next morning, I offered to cook us all breakfast. Dan's girl-friend informed me I had cooked the fry up the night before. I had no recollection of cooking anything. The blackouts were back. *Fuck.*

I busied myself preparing a goodbye meal in my place for Paula, her new husband and their friends before they moved to America. I agreed to start saving and go and visit them in three months, with a plan to join them out there. We had a great night. I had some wine to calm the hangover anxiety.

When everyone else was gone home I sat with the newly-weds and chatted about my love life or lack of. With encouragement from them I agreed to try the online dating scene.

I had boyfriends in the past, but I was single a couple of years now. Online dating was a new phenomenon to Ireland and to me. I let them create an online profile for me that night. They used a photo of me at their wedding wearing an off the shoulders electric blue dress with my hair in a long plait. This did not represent my everyday look. I felt like a fraudster.

There began the dating disasters, some on my side and some on the potential partners' sides. There was the guy who was full of himself who caught me drying my sweaty armpit patches in the toilet. There was the guy who announced at the start of the first date he wanted to wait until marriage for sex.

There was the arrogant guy bragging about all his properties. I paid for my coffee and left while he was in the toilet, admiring himself.

After months of online dates, I now fully justified my drinking. I was thinking *anyone who has endured online dating would know I needed the Dutch courage.* One guy, who was not really my type looks-wise, charmed me with his witty messages into meeting up for a date.

I turned up to a bar on Camden Street in Dublin City, twinkling lights everywhere and Christmas music. An arm outstretched to greet me, it was attached to a person I did not recognize. This man looked older than the man in the photo online. In fact, I think it was a completely different man.

I ordered a large glass of red wine and made some polite conversation. Before we finished that first drink, he ordered us another. I felt obliged to stay for longer.

In the middle of his babbling, he referred to himself in the third person and let his real name slip out. I tackled this lie and said out straight he told me a different name. He admitted he was signing off with a fake name.

I downed the second glass of wine and high tailed in my high-heeled boots out onto the street, so fast, that I slipped and fell flat on my back. I whacked the back of my head. I jumped back up and ran to the bus stop. As soon as I got home, I went online to delete the account, but I fell straight asleep.

I woke the next morning, the laptop was open. I slowly stretched out and hit the space bar. The screen lit up; there was message from the creep. I deleted it without reading it. I scrolled around with my settings on private and read people's profiles. I was afraid that they might think I was interested if they saw I read their profile.

A familiar face caught my eye. There on the screen was my blond buddy from years ago, 'Night Rider.' He had the shaved head minus the fringe now. His profile picture showed him in an army outfit.

I laughed at how one night of hand holding had caused me so much hassle. His profession choice alone reassured me that we had not been meant for one another. It was fun to see him, nonetheless.

There were a few meaningless messages and one from an attractive looking man, Charlie. *An honest to goodness name*, I thought. He looked interesting and normal. That was becoming a rare and attractive quality.

His photo portrayed boyish good looks and bright blue honest eyes, framed with earnest warmth. He looked unharmed by life with no obvious traces of crazy in his eyes. There was a solidness exuding from him on the screen. I messaged him back.

We spent a number of weeks messaging online. There was no crazy quirk revealed so I agreed to a date. I gave Paula the safety planning update, the exact location of our date. If I needed to leave, I would text 'go.' Then she was to call me with an emergency that I needed to attend to immediately.

I reminded Paula to keep her phone nearby because she is so forgetful. Once we were on a video call making plans, we were interrupted by a knock on her front door. 'Sorry I'll just answer this.'

I sat there watching her go to answer the front door to a woman, presumably a friend. She stood there chatting for a minute then went out the door. I waited for twenty minutes, but she did not come back. She completely forgot she was on a video call with me.

Paula reassured me she would remember and reminded me not to get drunk. That was because of how I was back then. Her husband had a nickname for me when I was drinking 'Cocaine Lucy.' Not because I was taking drugs at that time but because of how I was when I was drinking.

I dabbled in cocaine for a few months, years before. Paula found out and told Shane. I had no idea. I was sitting in Mam and Dad's one Sunday morning with a hangover, full of fear. As Shane walked by me, he flicked a rolled up fifty euro note at me saying, 'You might need that.' His tone was totally dead pan.

I nearly died. My cheeks reddened. I knew deep down it was a really bad idea to be snorting cocaine. The person I was seeing at the time, his friend was a cocaine dealer. It was so easy to partake in fancy hotel toilets or at parties with a free supply.

Afterwards I would promise myself I would not do it again. Then I would get drunk and forget my sober self. The anxiety the next day after having drink and drugs reached a new level. It was debilitating.

That one comment from Shane was enough to snap me out of that phase. I knew someone who cared about me, knew I was doing something wrong. Thank God Paula told him, and I stopped then.

Charlie asked me to meet for coffee on a Saturday afternoon. Butterflies accompanied me on the bus to the city centre. I stood outside Bewley's on Grafton Street. I asked Charlie to text me when he got there and headed into a clothes shop across the road.

I was worried I was over dressed for a lunch date in a knee-length black and green dress with dark brown knee-high boots and a chocolate brown leather jacket.

I was contemplating buying something else to change into when my mobile vibrated in my pocket. He texted to say he was there. I walked towards the exit. I stopped briefly and took a deep breath. As I walked towards Bewley's, Charlie was waiting for me. He was taking me in with a slight smile on his face.

I smiled when I saw him. His hair was tousled, and he had a black Regatta jacket and blue jeans on. He looked like he could as easily be on a windy beach as be on Grafton Street in the middle of Dublin city. We introduced ourselves and went inside.

I followed him up the stairs and we sat at a small table in the middle of a busy floor full of people. I ordered a hot chocolate and Charlie got a coffee. We began chatting. He looked younger than thirty-two. He had a sparkle in his eyes and a shy smile. As he spoke to me, he was almost looking out from under his eyebrows on occasion.

He told me all about himself. He was originally from the countryside. He was in a permanent job, as a Philosophy lecturer, for the previous fifteen years. He seemed settled. Unbeknownst to myself that scared me. I was nowhere near settled. I was the opposite.

We had another coffee and hot chocolate and then we left. It was raining and his car was parked in the other direction, but he insisted on walking me to the bus stop. As the bus arrived, he gave me a kiss on the cheek. I thought he was going for my lips and kissed his as they passed by mine for my cheek. We both acted like it did not happen. I chuckled on the inside.

Soon after that date he contacted me, and we met at a fancy restaurant in the city. I wore a killer blue short dress. I felt him watch me as I left the table to go to the ladies' room during the meal. We sat there talking for so long the waiter came and gave us the bill because they were closing.

We spent a lot of time together. When we were out in the city for lunches, we regularly dropped into the perfume shop Paula worked in. We cooked for each other in my apartment and in his house on the other side of the city.

After couple of months, I invited Dan to come by to my place for dinner straight from his rugby training. Charlie would be there too. I made baked potatoes. We were all attempting to eat them until Dan said, 'These rocks are lovely.'

The three of us laughed.

'I'm sorry; I forgot to wrap them in tinfoil.'

Charlie just smiled at me. I knew he did not care. I was more concerned about what Charlie thought of me still renting or not having a driving licence than my culinary chaos.

I worked in the same organisation for fourteen years, bar my stints in Australia and London. Now here I was in in a new job in a brand new career. It felt like starting over. He had been driving for years. I bought Paula's car, as she was not taking it to America but failed my test twice due to nerves and hangovers.

I hoped he was not what myself and some of my friends called 'box tickers.' I knew it was very hypocritical of me. I did not want him to judge me but there I was doing that exact thing.

Deep down, I was intimidated by Charlie. He seemed together. His looks were boyish, but he was a man. I still felt like a girl. Not a woman yet. I tried to park my insecurities.

Charlie did not drink. That made it easier for me not to drink when I was with him. He said he had his years of going to gigs and pubs and he had outgrown the party days.

He had the summer off from lecturing. Often after a game of golf he met me in the city when I was finished work. We met at the Garden of Remembrance and sat in the sun, chatting before the cinema or one of our long dinner dates.

Parallel to lovely dates with Charlie I was not enjoying the new role as a children in care social worker. When we were together it was fun and relaxed. In work it was the opposite. There was a huge two-year backlog of cases to be addressed retrospectively, alongside new cases.

The birth parents and the foster parents had their own individual social workers. My role was primarily to support and advocate for the children in care. They were amazing.

To be placed in care there was a sad or disturbing story, and this unsettled me. Every time another beige file or a pile of them landed on my desk I dreaded knowing the contents. Children are taken into care if they are being neglected or abused or are at strong risk of it and this made for sad reading.

The responsibility of trying to protect and safeguard the children from any further potential abuse, harm, neglect or sad circumstances was huge. Trying to do it at high speed, to hit the ground running and to be thorough was stressful.

The role was also exceptionally paperwork heavy. I was unnerved and saddened by the weight of all this and seeing families split apart. I found it difficult to relax outside of work. Charlie's company was my favourite part of the week, yet I was afraid to tell him how I felt. I hoped I could grow to enjoy the job, so I kept quiet.

I was feeling heartbroken about Paula's move to America. We had been so close for years, travelling together, living together on and off. For years we spoke on the phone daily on the way to work and often in the evenings too.

Paula had been working in the perfume shop near Trinity during the four years I was there. I regularly appeared there for emergency chats to ease the nerves or a hangover. Mostly before a presentation. I always left feeling and smelling better.

I did not know what I was going to do without her. She was one of my best friends from babyhood until now in our thirties. We always said growing up we would be neighbours.

Paula encouraged me to start saving properly and to come and visit at Christmas. I heard that social workers were supported and treated better in America, so I agreed. Private social work existed over there. They worked in close teams and had a pool of cars. It was such early days with Charlie, I did not think it was an option to ask him to come too.

At that time, I cried every morning before work from the anxiety of it. The tears flowed along with the shower many mornings. I gave myself that chance to have a cry. Then I would take a deep breath, have a cup of tea and put my makeup on. No one knew.

I got through the morning and went to the park for lunch and to eat an ice cream to cheer myself up. That was when I took a lunch break. There was a culture of the social workers working through breaks and staying until eight in the evening.

I was instructed to check a depressed mother's fridge and presses for the vodka my supervisor suspected she was hiding. I just could not bring myself to do it.

I did not want to police people. I wanted to sit with them and figure out what hurt them so much that they did not love themselves. Of course, I did not share this with my team.

I believed I was a square peg in a round hole and in the wrong role. I envied the family support workers. I would have preferred to be doing that. Supporting parents or foster parents in a pragmatic way. When I was in London, I did something similar.

I was assigned to a family, a mother with eight children. She smoked hash all day. I cleaned up the house and changed nappies. I remember giving two of the children a bubble bath. They never had one before; the excitement from them was immense. Afterwards, I treated them for lice and combed the nits out of their lovely little heads.

I would have preferred that, than this case managing but I felt I had to stay in the job. I had gone back to college for four years to train as a social worker. I refused to admit that I did not love, or even like the career I had chosen to train in.

This plan B of mine was shaping up to be fairly shite. I was in my thirties. I did not have another four years of studying and scrimping financially in me.

All of this reinforced the idea that it might be better if I went to America. I felt it was the best of my limited options. I was finding it harder to hide how I was feeling about the job. I told Charlie the basics of how difficult it was.

He tried to console me: 'You know you're not a caged animal. A permanent job is actually a good thing Lucy.'

I wanted to tell him I felt exactly that way. I was thinking, *Christ, Charlie, doing this permanently feels like a life sentence. In fact, jail would be more fun. I'd read loads of books, maybe even write one. I wouldn't be responsible for these beautiful little children. I wouldn't have to be constantly on the edge of a panic attack.*

Instead, I just lied. 'Yeah, I know Charlie, you're right.'

The worse I felt the less I met up with Charlie. I searched for ways to cope with the stress. I went to a homeopath as I was getting lots of headaches. She turned out to be a process worker too. She was amazing and helped me to figure out ways to manage the stress by looking after myself better.

I was going to weekly meditation classes in the Buddhist Centre for the previous year. That gave me a greater peace of mind. I had some time off coming up, so I decided to go on a meditation retreat with some people from the Buddhist Centre.

I arrived at a large old farmhouse in Navan. The walls inside were painted white and the exposed beams were varnished dark brown. I felt the energy from all the previous retreats. Deep relaxation seeped into the walls over the years and wrapped me up in a gentle calming energy once I was inside.

I shared a dorm with five other females. Our bunk beds were tiny, cosy sleeping cocoons. The males had the same in their room. The coldness of the old house felt fresh and invigorating. It kept me awake too during teachings and the group meditations.

As I learned about Buddhism I understood that people are all born naturally Buddhist. We start out compassionate and believing the best in others and ourselves. Babies are calm and in the moment.

I have come to believe that life distracts people away from this: our true nature. Meditating, attempting to be mindful and trying to apply some of the Buddhist teachings, especially compassion can bring people back to that, including myself.

I can easily practice being mindful in any moment when I remember to do so. I have come to enjoy meditation, but my busy mind loves a good wander too.

I liked the Buddhist way of life they were teaching us about on the retreat. I am not saying I changed at that time. I did not. I became aware of what I needed to learn and how to do it. To become who I wanted to be. My best self.

I stored that information in my back pocket, and it really helped me later on. The Buddhist way of life seems like a good map for living a good life. If you follow the principles that it sets out, it creates fresh and clean living in mind, body, spirit, and also actions.

I knew I could meditate until I levitated but if I then drank ten pints of cider, did the dirty on my boyfriend and got sick on myself that was not going to take me into a mindful or wholehearted way of life.

I strived to find a place somewhere between the Buddhist and the boozer. Somewhere safe and sustainable. I knew I was never going to be super pure or even to be able to practice total self-discipline.

Paula once told me she did a ten-day retreat in India with an unopened packet of biscuits in her room and she did not eat them. I would not last ten minutes in a room with any packet of biscuits. I admired her discipline. I knew I was not transforming into a Buddhist ever. I was hoping to chill my mind out.

While on the retreat I found my meditation was regularly interrupted by thoughts of wondering where Charlie was and what he was up to. I missed him. I would have loved to text him if phones were not prohibited.

There was a period of silence for two days. We meditated, cooked dinner, ate and washed up together silently. We shared the dormitory bunks without making a peep.

I even took a country walk with three others and a random dog in silence. At the very beginning it was like one giant long extended awkward silence. That wore off and once I got used to being quiet, I enjoyed the break. I was even sad when the silence part of the retreat ended. It was a refreshing relief not having to communicate as much.

I have always been so talkative. I learned I need to be quiet too and process all the information and experiences coming at me and my senses. That was a good discovery for me. I am an introvert who does well at masquerading as an extrovert because I love people and their company.

I was still using masks at that time to reflect whatever face I thought the other person or people wanted to see or would approve of. That took a lot of energy out of me on a number of levels. I tend to need a period of processing and recovery after being with people to replenish.

There were hours of meditation daily. On the second last day we meditated for four hours. I still cannot comprehend how I sat still for that long. I was finding a deep sense of inner peace and managing to actually meditate.

I found out it was not about eliminating thoughts but extending the periods of quiet and calm between them. We did the Metta Bhavana meditation, whereby we sent loving kindness to ourselves for five minutes and then to a good friend.

Next, we sent loving kindness to someone we barely knew and then someone we found difficult. Then finally to all of them together. It was beautiful and I felt refreshed after days of being in the country relaxing. It was wonderful that my mind got a chance to rest.

After the Metta Bhavana meditation that evening, we were given a period for free meditation. We all sat together again. This time we were directed to witness our mind and watch the thoughts go through it like clouds.

After a short meditation, in my mind I saw a vastly expansive starry sky. Then I saw myself. I was red, yes red, and flying through the sky. It was like I could see the universe and it was three-dimensional. I flew to the edge of the universe, as it were, and it became two dimensional.

I saw myself pulling back the corner of the black star-studded universe sky. It looked like I was peeling the corner of a painting back. Then I was jolted back to reality. What an unbelievable experience it was.

I heard of blissful visualizations during meditation. This never happened me before and I had not been striving for it. Over dinner I mentioned it to two other people. They did not comment, possibly they thought I was going a bit crazy. I was fascinated and invigorated by the experience.

That evening we all sat by the fire for the nightly teachings from the leaders. They told us about 'Varanogi, the goddess of freedom and inspiration inspired.'

They described her as 'A red female figure flying through the sky.'

I was gob smacked.

7

*A*fter the retreat I met up with Charlie. We stayed up late talking and discussing spirituality. I went back to work feeling refreshed. My boss advised me that she had increased my already unmanageable caseload.

I was back to being paralyzed by the headaches and stomach pains. This was caused by the fear of not being able to attend to a child who might need me or if I missed something among all the cases.

Neglect is one of the hardest things to deal with. I asked myself, *what if I don't recognise a depressed or suicidal teen or a child who is being abused? What if I can't get to a helpless child quickly enough?*

Paula video called from America they were settled in Michigan, she asked if I was saving for my flight to visit at Christmas. I assured her I was. I explained how I needed to find a less stressful social work job.

I went out with Hilary that night and drowned my sorrows. After a few drinks I ended up telling her I needed to go to America so that meant I was going to have to break up with Charlie.

The next morning, he phoned and offered to come over to spend the day with me for my birthday. I was full of fear. I drank so much before, during and after the night out, cider, shots, and wine. The terrible trio. I was in bits. I felt sick and shaky.

I played it down to Charlie and agreed to spend the day together. I drank lots of water and took some painkillers. I had a shower and got dolled up, that helped me to look less hungover.

Charlie turned up, looking gorgeous. When I opened the door, he stood there with a big warm smile on his face. He was holding a beautiful white orchid in a pink plant pot. Without moving, he stretched out his arms and handed it to me. Like someone handing me their heart, his heart. I did not want to hurt it or him.

We had a lovely day at an exhibition in the city, and dinner in my favourite Japanese restaurant. He was full of chat and energy and we bounced off each other.

I was back in work on the Monday and back to planning my escape to America. I was full of anxiety again. I was afraid to let my feelings for Charlie get any stronger. I thought it would be best and fairest to him to end things soon. I started to shut down my feelings for him. I called him and cancelled some of our upcoming plans.

A few weeks later he cooked me a beautiful meal. He was chatting, talking about plans for renovating his house. I guessed he was envisioning me in the new scene. Then he mentioned me sitting in his new kitchen with him.

We went to bed and I did not sleep. At 5am, after hours of looking at the walls, I got up and got dressed. Charlie sat up, looking confused. 'What's going on? What are you doing getting dressed?'

'I think I should go home, Charlie.' I whispered.

'What? Why do you want to go?' he looked worried.

'I just need to be in my own place.' I could not look at him.

'Lucy, why so urgently do you have to be in your own

place? Tell me what's wrong.' He was out of bed now standing in front of me, his hands on my shoulders.

'Charlie, I'm sorry, I think we are going to have to break up. You're amazing but I need to go to America, how can we stay together if I know I'm going?'

He sat down on the edge of the bed with his head in his hands. 'Lucy, I don't want to break up.'

'But we will both get hurt if we stay together and then I go, I'm so sorry.' I collected up my cosmetics as we spoke.

'So, what have we been doing here, Lucy?' He was starting to sound frustrated so I stopped packing up.

'It's not as if I want to have to go to America but I can't stay in Ireland. social work here is horrendous.'

'Jesus, Lucy, I thought we have something special. I care about you.' Tears sat on the inner edge of his eyes ready to fall.

'I care about you, too; I didn't know I would hate this job. It's causing me so much anxiety trying to make myself like it.'

Charlie looked rattled by my words. I was too but it was too late to gobble them back up. He was also trying to wake up and process what he was being told. I had been thinking this was what we needed to do on and off. For him it must have seemed so sudden.

'Lucy, if you change your mind, let me know.' He seemed sort of defeated now.

I was utterly gutted too. I wanted to go to America. I did not believe we were together long enough to emigrate as a couple. It crossed my mind to say it, but I held back.

As I collected my belongings, he followed me around with a sad expression. I wanted to be the one to comfort him. I felt horrible for causing him to look and feel that way. It might have been easier if he was not as kind. It would have given me a reason to love him less.

Tears rolled down my cheeks as I left. He did not cry, he just said, 'I hope you figure out whatever it is that you're looking for or running away from.'

This bothered me because I did not feel I was running to or away from anything. I did not reply. I knew he was letting me go reluctantly. I suspected he was going to cry once I was gone. He was being strong considering how close we were. I knew I would miss him terribly.

That night I sobbed on the phone to Paula. She said she liked Charlie. That made me cry even harder. She listened to me for a while and then reminded me of the upcoming Earthsong camping festival.

Paula bought me a ticket to the festival before she left. The thoughts of a drink and drug-free camping trip was not cheering me up. Paula said it would be good for me.

I wondered if it was a big mistake to break up with Charlie. She reminded me it might make it easier to move to America. In that moment, I preferred the thoughts of ten days of intoxication to forget the job, the tyrant boss, and the love I had asked to leave my life.

I was already desperately regretting it. I cried myself to sleep that night and every night for the following week. I did not think changing my mind was a viable option. I believed it was better to go it alone and start again in America.

The following month the camping festival was a welcome distraction. I was desperately missing Charlie and crying sometimes when I thought about him. I was nervous going alone but I wanted to get away.

So off I went. I told myself I had been halfway around the world on my own so I would manage it. *What was ten days sleeping in a tent, with random people, in a field, while sober?*

I arrived at the massive field in my wellies and carrying my tent, feeling very small among five hundred people. I found a circle of thirty people to camp with. They were friendly, creative, and interesting folks.

I met up with a lovely girl who was a friend of Paula's. We pitched our tents beside each other and during the festival we became friends too.

We constructed a very basic home-made kitchen, made of wood. We also made a fire pit and put up a tarpaulin shelter from the sun or the rain. It was great to learn how to do it and to be back to basics. Being in nature all day was really good. I felt grounded.

Initially at the workshops I cursed Paula as I discovered how cosy it all was. I was getting lots of hugs from random strangers and not sure what to think. I am a hugger for sure, with everyone I know well. Strangers being so forward was unsettling. I enjoy keeping my personal space until I get to know someone.

On the first morning at the daily morning meeting, I was sceptical about the set up. There were roughly 400 of the 500 people there. We were all in this huge red and yellow topped tent.

One of the organizers produced an empty can of Heineken and everyone gasped loudly. I thought it was some sort of skit. *This has to be a joke, all the exaggerated gasps are like some-*

thing from a pantomime. It is one empty beer can. People drink them when they go camping. I exploded laughing.

The other hundreds of campers all looked at me silently and strangely when I laughed. It was not a joke or a skit. Everyone there wanted to have a sober experience. *Oh, for fuck's sake.*

Later that evening, I cursed Paula again when I discovered the showers were communal. Everyone got in naked. Yes, they were as bare bummed as when they were born and so was I.

She had failed to mention that there were three showers for hundreds of people to wash themselves, powered by a wood stove. There was often a queue of people waiting while you showered. In the same room, well, tent-type thing.

This was way out of my comfort zone. Actually, as far as possible as I could get. A fellow female camper tried to chat to me as we showered. I wanted to say *for the love of God woman, please don't make small talk with me while I am naked.* Instead, I tried to act like this was all normal. Naked chatting was fine with me, yes, this was super dandy.

After a couple of days, I smiled because I found myself enjoying dancing barefoot in a field as the sun went down. It was like something from a documentary that might be called 'People at one with the wild.'

There was a group of us dancing to some loud drums. I felt my legs and my whole body. This had never happened to this extent before. I felt very alive and happy. It was the same feeling of freedom as when I ran around in nature as a child with Shane, Paula and Dan. I called out in my mind to Paula in America, *you absolute fecker, this is actually great.*

I met all sorts of magical people. This was all new to me, a natural high from dancing in a field. No drink or drugs, just honest good fun was making people happy. The culture of the festival was to be kind and gentle, no cursing or phone use.

I shared my camping circle with a beautiful and spiritual older man and his charming wife, Adam and Brigid. They were in their sixties. Such gentle and real people. I was drawn to the well of the knowledge Adam appeared to have and the peace of mind he portrayed. He seemed at ease with himself and the world around him.

Life appeared to be Adam's playground, and this put others, including myself, at ease. He was always singing or humming and playing the guitar. It became the soundtrack to my experience at Earthsong.

Adam turned W.B Yeats's poem 'Innisfree' into an almost lullaby type song just him and the guitar. He sang, *I will arise and go now, go to Innisfree, a small cabin I'll build there, and I shall have some peace there, for peace comes dropping slowly.*

He explained to me how we all have our own Isle of Innisfree. His interpretation was that the poem is an invitation to live an empowered life. That we can all find the place where we feel free and at ease.

That sounded like something I was certainly interested in. I often got a lump in my throat when I listened to him because his voice tugged my heart strings strongly. He was so earnest but not in a sentimental manner, it was a healing voice. Everything he said I felt intuitively that it was true and coming from the heart.

Certain people we meet in life have that extra special magic about them. They seem to sprinkle it on everyone around them and he was one of those people. His wife was one of those warrior women. She was full of wisdom. Her confidence and strength rubbed off on me by being in her company.

Every morning at Earthsong I joined a huge choir of two hundred people singing and sometimes chanting in the big tent. It was called Heart Song. People often cried or smiled, and it seemed very healing. I was judgmental and thought it was a bit self-indulgent, *all that crying*.

I noted the same few people became inconsolable on a regular basis and privately named them *the cry-a-lots*. There was the occasional cathartic shaking going on too. I wondered was it staged. Despite myself I found it to be a beautiful experience and I went back most mornings.

One day I was singing and chanting a beautiful song with the group while others harmonized. I visualised Shane in a large field. I realized it was the field behind the house in Longford we stayed in on summer holidays as children. He was walking away from me, casually strolling in his jeans and loose shirt among the long grass towards another large field.

I felt it was him leaving. It did not bring me much peace, instead it made me sad to the core. I was not ready to say goodbye to him. I sat on the floor in the big tent, sobbing. Then, I became embarrassed that I was now one of, what I had termed *the cry-a-lots*. I do not like to cry in front of others.

An older woman with wild grey hair came and sat beside me. She put her hand on my shoulder. This gave me some strength. I mustered up the courage to look at her. She smiled at me. I dried my eyes and stood back up and sang with the group. I wished I knew where Shane was.

I learned a lot during that week and made some lovely friends. I returned feeling grounded after camping. All my belongings smelled like camp fire and I loved it. I was refreshed after not drinking for ten days. I had a new lease of energy and determination to not binge drink anymore.

I kept saving and planning for my trip. I emailed services in America for employment opportunities. I looked at potential accommodation online and booked my flights for Christmas.

Paula told me about the American people on the phone. 'They are lovely people, they don't gossip. In work if I bitch at all, even as a joke, I'm met with silence. Sure it was the opposite in the Dublin shop.'

'Ha, Paula, we know how you like a good old bitching session. When you and Kerry get together no one is safe.'

'Feck off, Lucy.'

She still had her Irish accent and seemed happy. I was looking forward to going over.

After my experiences at Earthsong, the culture of a society and how we treat each other was extra important to me now. According to Paula, Michigan seemed to be a good place to live. I was nervous and excited for the new adventure coming soon.

It was December now. It was a few months since I broke up with Charlie. Even though I missed him, I felt ready to start my new life.

I arrived to a lot of snow and a big open blue sky. It was freezing cold but very refreshing. It was a welcome change from the Irish grey winter sky. I stayed with Paula and her husband. They had been there months now. Paula was working in a local perfume store.

It was not what I expected at all, it was a different way of life. They were living in a remote area and seemed happy there. They showed me all the sights. The beach covered in snow was a whole new mystical sight to behold.

We took a road trip to the other side of Michigan to visit her husband's relatives. Paula was right, the people were amazing, so friendly and kind it was wonderful.

They stuffed us full of square meat feast pizza and beef pasties. I was never so glad my vegetarianism had ended after a night out in Australia years before. It was scrumptious; they were so warm and loving to us. It was almost overwhelming to receive such a homely welcome. I loved seeing what the real Michigan life was like. I enjoyed every minute of that experience.

On return to their place, Paula and I went to a baseball game. The buzz was brilliant. I was chatting excitedly when suddenly she asked me to stop talking. Back into my box I went quietly wondering *what the hell is her problem?*

She seemed to have changed a little, taking on her husband's quieter persona and by the looks of things she expected me to do the same. I was hurt and uncomfortable.

I did my best not to aggravate them by being too chatty on my visit but at times it was a bit awkward.

One thing that was easier there, was not to drink. Paula had never been a big drinker. When New Year's Eve came around, I was relieved we were going to their neighbour's house and not a bar. I did not know if I could abstain in a bar. I wanted to have a drink, but I also did not want to.

I could not trust myself not to overdo it. A lot of New Year's days had been spent pickled in cider, full of fear and not remembering what I did the night before. I knew that would not wash with Paula and I did not want to cause any hassle.

I held out nearly all night before I nervously sipped one glass of red wine at the very end of the evening alone in my bedroom. I then went straight to sleep before it took effect. I knew once it did, I would need more.

I did not trust myself anymore with alcohol. Yet I could not help myself. I had to celebrate New Year's Eve with even one drink.

I was surprised at the end of the two weeks in America that I did not want to emigrate after all. I was not ready to start a whole new remote life on my own. If they were based in the city, it may have been different.

Paula had her own family now. They were married a short while. I felt it was their adventure and I intended to leave them to build their life together.

I left with an extremely heavy heart. I would miss them, but it was a relief to go home to my own space and life again. I did not know what I would do without Paula. I cried all the way on the flight, wondering how I was going to figure out what I was going to do next.

I found a massive modern apartment to share with one other guy. He seemed a nerdy quiet type, so I snapped it up. I lugged all my belongings over in black bags.

Whenever I moved, I gave away or left behind items I did not need such as books and clothes so this move was easy. I set up my easel and disappeared for hours in the evenings into an oil painting of a charming white cottage in the country.

I soon became restless from a Thursday afternoon itching for something. By a Friday evening some cider scratched that itch. After another forty-eight-hour weekend session, I woke up early and full of fear. My head pounded as I tried to figure out how I got home or what I did the night before.

My brain felt like it had swelled around each rusty cog. With every clunky movement I felt the engorged mass bouncing off the inside of my skull. I wondered if I was dying. I half wished I could drive off the local harbour into the water. I was not a strong swimmer. I knew the cold and the depth would swallow up me and my fear fast.

I gave out to myself for not having a licence at thirty-three years of age. I told myself that if I had learned how to drive at the weekends, instead of always being hungover, that I could actually go there, to the harbour, in Paula's car and put an end to the pain.

I was on the edge of a panic attack. I wondered if I was losing my mind. I had to stop the dark thoughts. I wanted to live and the anxiety to end. I was shocked that I had blacked out again. I did not intend to. I never intended to. I felt drunk. I picked up my phone and saw I had a text from my own number. I opened it, baffled. I did not remember sending anything.

I read the text to find that I had sent a plan of how to end my own life. I had instructed myself to go down to the local train station. I was still under the influence but sobering up enough to be scared of how out of control I felt.

I looked for my keys everywhere. I was scared and unsure what I was going to do. The front door and back door were locked so I knew my keys had to be inside the house. I tried all the usual spots: in my handbag, my jacket, the kitchen counter and the hall table. I looked under my bed in case I had left them somewhere obscure because I had been so drunk.

Bending down caused me to gag. I had to run into the bathroom and vomit. It was all liquid, all alcohol. I kept vomiting until it hurt and all that was left was bile.

This happened countless times after drinking from the age of twenty. It is hard to replay it in my mind. It makes me anxious to remember how often I was physically sick from too much alcohol. I battered my liver, stomach and God knows what else.

I gave up the search for the keys and lay on the couch watching mind-numbing television, trying not to vomit. I had to do deep breathing not to have a panic attack because I was also locked into my house. The rest of that day was a blur of fear and vomiting.

That evening I was tidying my bedroom and spotted my angel tarot cards on my bedside table. I cringed at myself, thinking, *Right, so you did your angel cards last night totally locked.* I lifted the lid of the box up to tidy them back away and there were my keys. I truly believe the angels hid them from me because I was meant to live.

I lay on the bed, crying. I could not control how much I drank or what I might do to myself when I did. I was scared of myself. This was something new to fear. I quickly turned off my phone. I was unable to face reminders of the demons that came out to play during my blackouts.

I went down to the kitchen and sat at the table with a cup of tea. That comforted me always. I spotted the plant Charlie gave me on the window ledge. It was dead; it had been since before I went to America. I brought it with me

111

regardless. I was not willing to part with the beautiful pink plant pot.

I listened to the rain pelting down onto the skylight. As I sobered up, every drop was amplified in my raw state. I thought back to the many rainy nights last winter when Charlie was with me. I wished he was upstairs now.

My heart broke at the thought of him alone in his house maybe listening to the rain too. I did not enjoy the thought of him having company either. As tears fell off my chin, I knew I had to find a distraction to get through the alcohol-induced anxiety. There was no way I was going to sit around panicking or crying.

I grabbed an umbrella and went down to rent a DVD. That helped to distract me enough through the hours of being on the edge with anxiety. Hangovers were defined by the edgy feeling, and followed by a low mood. Then by that non-existent little shadow 'mouse' I used to think I saw out of the corner of my eye.

I had to go into the supermarket to get out some cash from the ATM. I kept my gaze down and prayed I would not see anyone I knew. Hangovers made me extremely self-conscious and almost paranoid.

It was as if I overdrew on exuberance and false confidence while drinking. The next day I had little, or nothing left. I was in the minus. The interest to be paid was all my self-worth and self-esteem. I would have to build it up again for the millionth time.

I found a film that was funny: an old reliable with a neurotic Jack Nicholson in *As Good As It Gets,* nothing violent or scary to make my anxiety worse.

I waited in the queue to pay. The lighting felt harsh, and I was sweating, involuntarily breaking into hot flushes because of all the alcohol in my system. Cider was seeping out my pours in an apple and acid aroma around me. My mouth was dry from dehydration and the feeling of dread in my stomach made me nauseous. I wondered how I felt these emotions so strongly and did not pass out.

Instead, I was standing there as if nothing was wrong. I likely looked normal to someone who did not know me. I paid and got out quickly. I decided I would find something to eat later when I eventually got hungry enough. It is not possible to experience fear and hunger simultaneously. Another shop, queue or an interaction with a person was unmanageable.

Once home I got a pint of water and some paracetamol and went to bed with the film. The relief that my bedroom-bound housemate was nowhere to be seen was immense.

My head was sore, but that was nothing new. At this stage it felt like there was a huge thick and tight elastic band around the top of my head at my temples for the previous three months. The less I drank during the week, the worse the pain got. It did not make sense to me. I was popping pain-killers daily, oblivious as to how often I was taking them before I had to visit my parents' house.

8

Mid film I was starting to feel calmer. I plucked up the courage to turn my phone back on, to check my texts and calls history for clues as to how I got home. I was going to check my bank balance to see if I had anything left in there.

I had four missed calls from Sissy. I rang her back. We normally comforted each other over the mayhem of the night before and compared our levels of 'the fear.'

She bluntly announced. 'I'm on my way over. I need to talk to you.'

'Ok, see you soon.'

Sissy arrived and blurted out. 'I need to get the taxi fare from last night, the extra charge.'

'What taxi fare?' I asked her and myself.

She commented, 'Seriously look at the state of you Lucy. Do you not even remember what happened on the way home?'

We sometimes had those kinds of jokes with wild exaggerations of what the other person did the night before. There was an unfamiliar edge to her tone. My heart was beating faster now. This did not seem like a joke at all.

I offered an apology, 'Is everything ok, Sissy? I don't remember coming home. I'm sorry.' I did not want to hear the answer.

Sissy spat out, 'We hadn't even finished the main course, never mind got as far as my party in the pub before you were legless and acting the fucking eejit.'

As she spoke, I had a flash back of a jug of Captain Morgan's and a jug of Mojito on the restaurant table. They were to share among a table of eight of us. There were bottles of red and white wine too. I was drinking cider. I had cider while getting ready beforehand too. I suddenly saw myself having my fair share of the two jugs and some red wine.

I had zero recollection from the night except for the first hour. I had demolished all that alcohol. I found some of Sissy's other friends pretentious. I believed they thought they were a bit too cool refusing to drink in certain pubs that were too mainstream. I was hoping I had not shared my thoughts with them.

Sissy went on to inform me, 'I had to leave my birthday meal, with all my friends before it was over to escort you to a taxi. You were so drunk the taxi man wouldn't take you on your own.' She was almost spitting her words at me.

'Oh, shit sorry, Sissy.'

She continued, 'Oh well, it gets better. I had to go with you to your apartment. On the way you puked on me, yourself and the seat.'

She moved closer as if to impress upon me, 'The taxi man went fucking mad. He insisted we get out, he charged us a cleaning fee of *fifty fucking euro*. Lucy I'd to walk you the rest of the way and bang down the door until your oddball house mate appeared. You couldn't even remember the front door code. I put you in your pyjamas, I put your sick-covered clothes in the bath. I'd to clean myself with a towel and get a taxi back home. By the time I was home I was too pissed off to get ready again to meet everyone in the pub.'

She missed her meal and party because of me. I felt so guilty and embarrassed. I could barely look at her. 'I'm so sorry. I'll make it up to you bigtime. God. Maybe I should've eaten more.'

Sissy took a deep breath and then said, 'I don't want to have to say it to you, but you *need* to cop on, like how many shots *did* you have?'

Oh God there had been shots too. No wonder I vomited. I never saw her so serious or annoyed with me before. I did not blame her. I had been an utter ass. 'I don't know.'

I was scared at how little I remembered and how early in the night I had blacked out. Normally it was the end of the night I did not remember. My face alternated between reddening at the anger coming from her and paling with the nausea waves.

While she was saying all this to me, I started defending myself in my head, *sure you drink more than me, smoke loads, snort coke, it's not like I'm drinking every day.*

Suddenly it appeared she was reading my mind, as best friends can. She swiftly reminded me, 'Sure remember the state of you on the night out last month. You were trying to kiss the bloody barman, Lucy. You drank pint after pint of cider even when I was telling you to take a break.'

Sissy had no idea I had to do that to push down my own lack of confidence. Being a chameleon was hard and exhausting and alcohol made it easier, or so I thought. I tried to divert back to the most recent fuck up. 'Sissy, I promise the fifty euro will be in your account tomorrow.'

I had no idea if I even had any money left in my account. She mustered up a thank you. It was obvious she was fed up with me. I again said I was sorry. I meant it. I knew I would be lost without her.

Sissy was one of my best friends and a rock for me after Shane died. She left and I went back to try watch the film. I felt very low and full of anxiety.

After a couple of hours, I got up feeling uneasy. I wanted to tell someone, my family or a friend I was struggling to stop drinking. I did not know if they would understand. My usual drinking buddies, there were lots of them, would have laughed at me and bought me a drink to cheer me up. I worried my less drinking buddies would judge me.

For the next while I avoided all drinking situations. I tried to stop on my own, again. It was hard to figure out how to make myself feel a bit better.

I started to listen to spiritual and inspirational speakers online. I put their quotes around the place. They all essentially said the same thing: Do not drink, learn to love yourself, be aware of negative thoughts that lead to unhealthy behaviour such as alcohol addiction.

I repeatedly reminded myself: *watch your thoughts and do not get attached to them.* I put '*Just watch*' on a post-it on my mirror. This was to remind me my mind was the sky, and my thoughts were clouds to watch them as they go by and to just observe them. *Be like Buddha.*

I liked the sound of being a chilled out character relaxing under a tree. This was easier said than done. I was a long way from being there.

I had acquired some new unwelcome companions. Three extremely wild huskies accompanied me everywhere I went. They were untameable. I still had Mam's Misery, but now these three huskies were with me too. I was permanently walking them and attached to their leads while they pulled me in every different direction, simultaneously.

I named them: Fear, Sadness, and Anxiety. I tried to tame them by walking them along the seafront at every opportunity, listening to 'Revelate' by The Frames. They had to be trained to calm down. I did not know how, except to change my environment again.

I moved out from the apartment with the guy who stayed in his room. I packed up my things and once again took special care of the plant Charlie had gifted me. I missed him more than ever.

I moved in with a lovely nurse. I was glad to have company again. The stress of the social work job was not helping matters. It was not going to be possible to stay off booze, deal with the case load and the nut case of a boss.

I handed in my notice. The relief was immense and simultaneously I felt like a failure. I told myself, *you just are not able for it*. I wrapped up my identity in being a social worker. I graduated and bagged a really good job.

I returned to social care overqualified. I had to take a good look at myself and challenge my ego. It did not matter what I was doing once I enjoyed it and I was good at it. It took a while for me to truly let go of the fact that I was not going to be a social worker, even though I never really wanted to be one in the first place.

I got a job in a new organization as an instructor in a service for young adults with learning disabilities. I suggested I would teach them mindfulness and facilitate art classes alongside their educational and practical lessons. To my delight they agreed, and it was a lot of fun.

They had mild learning disabilities and said things to me like, 'Talk about our ability and not our disability.' They inspired me with their positivity and resilience. I was back in my comfort zone and the anxiety reduced dramatically.

Meanwhile, I was still going to the homeopath. She was full of wisdom and helped me to save my own life. I was still having the giant elastic band headaches. I thought she might have a remedy to help. The anxiety was less overall but it when it arrived it came in overwhelming waves. It was debilitating.

I told her what happened at Sissy's birthday and she again suggested, 'Maybe you're allergic to alcohol? Once you have one it sets off a physical craving and you cannot stop.'

I asked her, 'Are you saying I'm an alcoholic?'

She replied, 'What happened to your plan to stop drinking for one year?'

I had no answer. I tried and I had failed. I had tried so hard to stop drinking on my own, every year since Shane died.

Every New Year's Eve I resolved to have a year off alcohol and proceeded to wake up pickled in cider. I took homeopathic remedies, changed what I drank, tried to have none and tried to have one. It always led to more. One was never enough, and neither was ten.

She was right: once I started, I could not stop. It was eight years later and here I was drinking to blackout. I had not stopped.

I had willpower in every other area of my life when I wanted to. I could not fathom why I could not exert will power over my drinking once I started.

I sat there crying and baffled at how I kept defying my own will not to drink over and over. I was so tired. I told her 'I feel like I'm on a hamster wheel and I cannot get off.'

She said, 'A twelve step recovery meeting would be good for someone like you, Lucy.'

I thought to myself, *Right so, recovery meetings must be good for people who are grieving, that's what she means. She's not saying she thinks I'm an alcoholic, just that meetings would be good for me.*

'Ok, I'll try it.' I agreed to go, just like that.

I was so tired and depleted from all the trying and the severe hangover anxiety. I did not know where else to go. I thought I would take a trip to a recovery meeting and eliminate the possibility of being an alcoholic.

I planned to find out the real reason I was drinking so much and so often. Then I would know why I did not stop drinking once I started. Then I could drink like a normal person. They would show me how.

I went online and found a local meeting and off I went. I parked the car miles away so no one would recognize the car. I arrived at a church near where I grew up. I was terrified in case anyone would know me. It was dark and the church was empty. I saw light and heard chatter from a room at the back. I took a deep breath. Walking through a mostly dark church is a bit eerie.

I was glad to go into the room. People were drinking tea, chatting, and laughing. I wanted to say, *Hey, I'm Lucy and I'm not an alcoholic. I'm here to prove that and get back to drinking again. If you can tell me how to do that then that would be perfect.*

A woman in her early thirties, educated and employed, like me, shared her story. She said how she binge drank for years and blacked out repeatedly and how it was not normal.

My mind whirled. *What? Blackouts are not normal? That is not what getting drunk is?* I asked myself, *how have I been so stupid?* I had seen Dad like that so often, my aunties and uncles too. No one ever suggested they should stop or seemed to think it was not ok. I assumed it was normal.

At the first meeting I found out why I did not stop drinking once I started. It was apparently because I am an alcoholic. Yes, a young, educated woman, who does not drink daily can be an alcoholic. *Huh?* It was as if someone had hit me with stun guns on both my temples simultaneously.

I had a look back over my life, trying to find when I drank like a normal person. I found I always drank too much. From those first two cans of Ritz at age fourteen being downed in minutes with Brona, to Sissy's blackout birthday booze barfing. I drank to the point of blackout repeatedly.

I used alcohol to celebrate success or to drown my sorrows. At home or abroad, single or not, it did not matter. It never occurred to me what I was doing was unhealthy or wrong or I should stop, except that it caused me anxiety.

I believed it was grief and hurt resurfacing, not that those negative emotions were caused by alcohol. There was always a good reason, a good pub, and some company, sometimes which was better than others. Yet I was not willing to admit I am an alcoholic myself or accept it.

At the very first recovery meeting I heard to qualify as an alcoholic you did not have to drink every day. You had to not be able to stop. They said the only requirement for attendance at the recovery meeting was a desire to stop drinking. That made it a bit easier for me to accept being there. I did not have to decide if I was an alcoholic there and then.

I wanted to stop drinking. The people there were calling it a disease and saying they had to get sane and stay well. I was offended at the notion of not being well. I thought, *how dare they imply I'm crazy? I drink because I have problems; drink is not my actual problem, duh.*

They essentially imparted that they were recovering from a disease called alcoholism. I was both horrified and relieved, I identified with so much of what the members, aka the alcoholics, were sharing.

My mind was boggled as to how I ended up at a recovery meeting. It is not exactly what any of us dream of as a child. *Hey, Mammy, when I grow up, I want to be an alcoholic.*

Three questions kept whizzing around my head: *Fuck, how is this happening to me? How did I let this happen? Could I have stopped if I tried harder?*

I felt so fragile and decided it was best not share this new found revelation of my being a visitor to the recovery meetings club with any family or friends.

I wondered what my parents would say if they knew I was going there. Dad would probably go mad if he knew how much I had been drinking over the years. Whenever he saw me on a Sunday, usually armed with a fizzy drink to try to settle the nausea he would ask me, 'I hope you were not overdoing it last night?'

I always said, 'No I wasn't, Dad.'

Maybe he suspected something. I was not prepared to admit this new discovery to myself yet, let alone accept it and share it with others.

I was well aware of all the stigma. Part of me wanted to say to the people in the recovery meeting, *all you sober people in recovery are the ones who are the strongest to get yourselves back on track. You are a good bunch; people should know what a real alcoholic looks like.*

There was a big mix of everyone and anyone there from painters to politicians and from judges to janitors. Alcoholism does not care who you are, where you are from or what you do. Once you will drink yourself silly it will take you hostage. I was starting to realize that.

It felt like a matter of life and death to me now because it was. I had to go to meetings to stay away from the first drink, so I would not keep drinking into oblivion. Early recovery was not easy; it took a lot of hard work. I did not go into a treatment centre.

Instead, I did what is recommended and I went to ninety meetings in ninety days, for people who are new to the recovery program. I continued to go to the same meeting in the church where I went to my first recovery meeting. I went every week even though initially I did not want to go.

I certainly did not want to be an alcoholic, but I did have the desire to stop drinking. I just had to say goodbye to alcohol first.

Off I went to a hen party and for my last fling with my old flame cider. I had to say a final farewell. It was weird having a head full of recovery advice and a belly full of cider and shots.

It was a strange experience, almost like an out of body one. I watched myself shimmy around the dance floor, then outside to the beer garden to chain smoke.

I had to end the love affair with alcohol to be able to part with the cigarettes too. There was more drinking and dancing. I separated from the group, dancing on my own feeling fucked and not knowing which way to turn.

Eventually I went outside and had two last cigarettes in a row. I traipsed out behind the hen party to the hotel, a fake smile on my face and I went straight to bed.

I woke the next day in a fog of fear and still feeling drunk. I went home and returned to the recovery meeting. I properly started my ninety meetings in ninety days. I began grieving for my oldest companion, the one that never let me down. My confidence and magic forgetting potion: alcohol.

During the ninety days I went through a lot of emotions and only slept for six hours per night for the first six weeks. My whole back, every single inch, broke out in spots. It was severe and it took me a few days to realise what was happening. I was detoxing. I was grateful it only occurred on my back where it could not be seen.

At the end of the ninety days, I took up the role of secretary in the recovery meeting, this meant I had the keys to the church. It was up to me now to open the meeting and to make sure there were biscuits and milk for the tea. I had to find the first speaker of the evening who would do the chair. I believed this small but important responsibility would keep me going back.

I was starting to feel better, and I was well aware it was a bad idea to trust my ability not to start drinking again. Members warned me now that I was marginally better, if I was left to my own devices, I might easily forget I have a disease and how bad it got for me.

In the recovery meetings I heard people say that alcoholism is cunning, baffling and powerful. It is the only disease that will tell you, you do not have it. That scared me a little.

I agreed to be secretary because at least this way if I did not turn up someone may notice I was missing. I felt I did not want to have to become a member of the recovery meetings and I was scared of the stigma. Yet the thought of any more drinking binges where I did not know what I would do, or how I might end up filled me with dread.

I did not want to have to keep pulling myself out of hungover despair. I could not guarantee myself I would be able to stop after one drink.

A couple of months into doing secretary I was contacted from the manger in the organisation in Boston where I did my social work placement. While there I was very clear I did not want to leave and once I was qualified, I would love to go back. She remembered and informed me they had a sister organisation in New York and a social work role.

They were interested in interviewing me to work with Irish immigrants. Despite getting hammered drunk and falling asleep in my fancy frock in the Irish consulate's luxurious bathroom and being found by this manager, she was recommending me. She requested my contact details for the New York office, and I gave them.

Once again, I was swept up in the promise of a new life in a new place. A new start, again, where no one would know me. I eagerly awaited the contact from New York. I knew I was overqualified for the job I was doing.

This opportunity was not a scary social work role like the children in care one that caused me loads of anxiety. This was much different. There would be an Irish community. There would be craic to be had and a great social aspect.

I toyed around with all this and arranged a meeting with the manger via video call. Afterwards, I went through all the pros in my head. There was loads that outweighed the cons. Except for one.

It hit me like a slap in the face. *Wait a minute here, Lucy, if you go to New York there is no way you will stay sober, absolutely no one knows you there.* I asked myself, *is this a terrible idea or a brilliant one?*

I thank God I was thinking clearly enough to know, I was fooling myself into thinking it would be a good move for me. Yet the gremlin of alcoholism was throwing its gunk all over my clarity. Its sticky slime was trying to drown out the well voice in my head so I would feed it with cider once again.

It tried to convince me, *you could probably get away with it over there, Lucy. The only real problem was you kept trying to stop.* My will was changing rapidly. My mind was churning over the possibility of living as an active alcoholic.

On the other hand, I was pleading with myself, *think through the decision further because maybe you need to stay this time.* I came close to not doing the right thing which would have been to jet off to New York and live a life of debauchery.

I stayed to face my demons and to stay sober. For once I did not run. I had been running so fast, for so long, but this time I had to stay on the recovery road.

If I veered off it, I may never get back on it again. The shiny lights of New York had to be replaced with the streetlamps of north Dublin for me. I needed to stop moving house and changing jobs too.

It is suggested in the first two years of recovery not to get into a relationship or make big decisions. But I wanted to be well and fast. I had a new found lust for life. The recovery meeting fellowship replaced cider as my new scaffolding while I used the twelve-step programme to rebuild myself and my life.

I made a decision from then on to do what was suggested to me in the recovery meetings but only by people who were well and happy and living their lives to the fullest.

The first woman who helped me told me if I kept a plant or animal alive for two years then I would be ready for a relationship. I definitely was failing in the plant stakes. I had Charlie's plant, now a dried ornament but I was not letting it go.

I decided to go down the pet route, so I acquired a new kitten, Rosie, the cutest grey kitty you ever saw, with white paws and a white nose. She was a great source of comfort and distraction in the early days. I sat on the kitchen floor for what felt like hours playing with her.

Some of the things I heard at the meetings I knew were for people whose lives had fallen apart around them. They had lost jobs, families, partners, and their houses. I did not lose all of these things, except for Charlie.

I was realising, at times I also lost my way in the world. I was hearing stories about unwell parents or parents who drank too much. I was starting to realise the environment I grew up in was not very healthy. I was relieved being sober was helping me find my way back to my real self.

My pattern had been to always return to the pub and to go drinking no matter how many bad hangovers and experiences

I endured. I now had a healthy fear of my own free will. I had to go to the meetings.

I even grew to enjoy the first church meeting. I went to other meetings every week too. I cycled to a lovely local 'Promises' meeting on a Sunday morning. The meeting focused on what the original members of the recovery meetings promised you get if you stay sober. A new freedom from dependency on alcohol and happiness. This was my new focus, thinking of the benefits of staying away from alcohol.

I learned I need to do it one day at a time for the rest of my life. The longer I stayed away from drink, the more promises came true for me. I learned to practice gratitude too, as it was suggested at meetings. This became a huge factor in keeping me positive and well and happy.

I became interested in the notion, what you think about you attract. The law of attraction or intention. I believe where you focus your energy is what you draw to yourself. Daily if I list all the things I am grateful for in my life that make me happy. I will attract more of those things or experiences.

Initially I was not grateful to find myself having to attend the recovery meetings. I listed things I was happy about in my head each evening as I did the dishes. I gave thanks for things like my kitty; it was easier to be with her than people some days. I faked it, until I felt it and it worked for me.

It was also suggested to newer people to do the twelve steps with a sponsor. I did not entertain the idea of a sponsor as I did not see myself as a fully-fledged alcoholic. I was not bad enough that I needed to be told how to tie my shoelaces.

I did not try to find a sponsor but a decent and well, older woman helped me understand the program. She told me I was doing great and to be proud of myself. This was not possible as I felt so ashamed for not being able to control my drinking in the first place. I felt stupid for not knowing I had a problem. The denial has been so strong.

I cried a lot on my own because I believed it was going to be impossible to love myself because I hated one fact about myself. I was an alcoholic. There was a voice in the back of my mind saying, *sure maybe you are not, Lucy. Do you want to have to go to these meetings for the rest of your life? Jesus no.* Was the answer. Clearly, I asked myself a lot of questions and gave myself the answer I want. I cannot even blame the drink on that. It must be the insane streak I was so vehemently denying.

I found humour to be a good way to cope too. I learned to laugh at myself more. But the notion of being an alcoholic made me feel less than others and I was horrified of anyone finding out *about me.* It took nine months before I had one good feeling about myself again. It was fleeting but it was a start.

I was thirty-four years old. For the first time since I was fourteen years old, I woke up sober on New Year's Day without drinking one drop for the previous nine months. I felt so fresh and healthy and even happy. I thought *well a baby is born after nine months, maybe there is hope for me too.*

I was learning alcohol makes people who they are not. Not who they are. I was also so grateful to be alive and if I must have a disease, it is one there is a solution for.

Diabetics must take insulin and watch what they eat. The meetings are my insulin, and the twelve-step programme is my diet. I forgave myself for having an allergy rather than being a defected person. I began making plans and goals for myself. Friends at the recovery meetings kept saying to let my higher power guide me and make the decisions for me.

This was confusing, I asked the woman who was helping me 'How am I supposed to know what my higher power wants me to do? Like, how do I tell if my higher power wants me to have a cup of tea? I know this is stupid thinking for a half intelligent person, maybe my brain is a bit pickled from the booze.'

She explained, 'It's a matter of making a decision but you leave the outcome of that decision to your higher power.' It finally became clear. I had to stop trying to control the way things work out.

I know many non-alcoholics who struggle with wanting to control their own lives. Alcoholics are basically the same as everyone else except I believe a lot of us are rawer. I can only speak for myself, but I am definitely a more sensitive version of a human.

Lights, noise, negative energy, harshness in the world it hurts me that little bit more. I have been told I am an empath. All I know is I feel a lot and I can usually tell how another is feeling and it can be exhausting. At the same time, it can also be very easy to connect and communicate with people.

If I surround myself with positivity and healthy people places and things, I get to experience contentment, ease, and joy in bucket loads.

After one year of going to meetings and not drinking I finally admitted it to myself that I am powerless over alcohol. I am allergic to it. If I have one drink it sets off a craving in me where no amount of drink is ever enough. If that is defined as alcoholism, then I have it.

I prefer to think I have an allergy to alcohol rather than I am an alcoholic. I am lots of things, so I do not define myself by one. When I saw the patterns clearly there was no denying it to myself anymore.

Despite the years of pickling myself with cider and the crippling hangovers, I thought I was having an adventure and I kept going. I was living out Einstein's definition of madness: I was doing the same thing repeatedly and expecting different results.

9

I believed I was the same as all my friends who binge drank too. I learned that alcoholics are often the last to know we are sick. That is why we can look crazy to others, when we continue to drink too much too often. I did not even try to hide my drinking during my twenty-year career. To me it seemed normal.

As far as I was concerned my family and friends all did the same. My friends likely did stop before they entered blackouts, but I never knew that. My alcoholism was so anonymous I did not even know I was one.

I was not consciously in denial; I was unaware of my illness or disease. I wondered, *did my subconscious keep it that way, was my drinking a coping mechanism?* An incredibly unhealthy one, but one, nonetheless. After all, alcoholism is the one disease that tells you that you do not have it. Now I had admitted it to myself at long last. I was capable of accepting it too.

I wanted to tell my family and friends, but I did not know if they would understand. Dad's response to most things was to either blame me or get angry at me. I feared his reaction.

I was careful not to get drunk too often around my family, except Paula and Dan. I was very tempted to tell them. I felt alone with this new information about myself. I held off for another while. It was hard to gauge what their reaction would be, and I wanted to be strong enough to handle it.

I knew regardless of their opinions, this was a positive turning point for me, brought about by a negative disease. It caused me to build walls around myself from those who loved me. Yet to open myself to others I barely knew. It made me get it all a bit backwards at times.

I delved further into spirituality. I believe the suffering I experienced through alcoholism brought spiritual awareness for me. Alcohol brought me to the dark night of my soul. If I take out dark night, then alcohol brought me to my soul.

After another month or two I told Paula on a video call, 'You know the way you were always telling me to end the love affair with cider?'

'Yes.'

'Well, I did. I'm not drinking anymore and I'm going to recovery meetings now to stay off the drink.'

To my utter disbelief she said, 'That's good, but sorry I don't get it, Lucy.'

'Well apparently, Paula, if you are an alcoholic once you have one drink it sets off a craving and it's very hard to stop, so I think that's what happens to me.'

'This does not really make sense to me. I'm just not sure how I can support you. I don't really understand it.'

I was honestly baffled by her reaction. Here I was spilling out the scariest secret of my soul and she had no kind words for me. All the tears I mopped up for Paula and she was not willing to witness me, as I was, or to have a meaningful conversation.

She did not suggest she would do some research and get back to me. It seemed so lacking in effort. I felt let down and hurt after looking out for her over the years. 'Ok, well I wanted you to know,' I said defeated.

She moved on as if I had mentioned the weather. This caused me to wait longer before telling anyone else.

A few weeks later I told Kerry. She gave out to me for not telling her sooner and did not say much else. I wanted to be the one to tell my parents before Kerry, so I called out to my parents' house.

I landed into the artificial fire, on stiflingly warm, at full blast and the television on. They were in their usual spots in the sitting room. The kitchen table, which they have in their sitting room, was full of the remnants of cheese, crackers, nuts and crisps.

Snacks Dad had likely been driving Mam mental with by his noisy munching and crunching on them all afternoon. She referred to him as 'Hollow Head' because he was such a noisy eater.

Mam was alert. They were sitting half swallowed up on their big sofa. I sat in the rocking chair a couple of feet away and I engaged in a reasonable amount of chit-chat.

Then, with a dry mouth and my heart beating fast, I said, 'I have something to tell you.'

They looked at me expectantly while I told them, 'I had a bit of a problem with drink. I've been going to recovery meetings for the last year.'

Mam stayed quiet while Dad, as he was jumping up towards the kitchen door, said, 'Hold that thought.'

He instantly returned with half of a bottle of white wine and a glass. As he filled it up, he said, 'Now, you don't mind if I do.' It was the middle of the afternoon.

He proceeded to hide the bottle under his shirt in an exaggerated way. He was grinning at me, with an expression that said now you cannot get it.

I was relieved Mam was not upset by my revelation.

Within two weeks Kerry was giving me hassle. I asked to meet in a restaurant instead of a pub and she told me.

'You live in Ireland, sure there is drink everywhere, you are going have to get over it Lucy.'

I was deeply hurt and wondered had my sisters always been this dismissive of me or was I only noticing now.

Dan was kind and tried to be supportive. He gave me a hug and said, 'I love you, Lucy. If you're an alcoholic, then half the country probably are too. Sure, with the Irish drinking culture the way it is so many people can get away with it.'

I had not gotten away with it. I had become suicidal at the end. It was not up to me to convince him of anything. I simply told him 'I love you too. Thanks Dan. I'm here for you too, ok?'

'Ok, Lucy.' He agreed, smiling with kind eyes.

We went on nights out and he bought me soft drinks without comment or fuss. I think he knew it was not easy initially. He treated me pretty much the same as he ever had, except I was not invited to as many drinking celebrations.

Although that hurt me, I understood because I used to be glad if Paula went home early from parties. Then she would not see or relay my antics to me the next day with a frown on her face.

I knew if Shane was alive, he would be kind and supportive too. I was sure he was one of the angels that hid my keys on me that night to stop me going to the train station.

In those early days of recovery, I looked through the photographs to try to piece together where I had stepped over the line with alcohol. I found some old letters from when I had been in London and Australia.

There was one was from Shane. He was talking about his plans to work in the area of horticulture. I cried for the future he missed out on. At the end of the letter, he said he missed me, but he was glad I was enjoying my adventure. He said I had a lot going for me and, 'You have a great ability to get on with people.'

If ever I needed a boost of confidence, it was then. Things were strained with Kerry, she was angry at me because I would not visit her more often and for longer, yet she would not visit my house. It was impossible to resolve things because she would not communicate with me properly.

Dan's wedding was the first big event I attended sober. Paula was home from America and the whole family was together.

Although Paula had been suggesting to me for years to 'stop getting so dangerously drunk', 'you need to end the love affair with cider, anything could happen you when you are that far out of it on the drink.' Yet she seemed to be playing along with Kerry and my parents. They were ignoring that I told them I was an alcoholic and that I was in recovery.

Dad and Mam both offered me wine on different occasions. I complained to Paula assuming now that time had gone by, she would understand why I could not drink. She told me, 'They don't believe you, Lucy, they don't think you are an alcoholic.'

I was flabbergasted. This was a new level of crazy. It would have been easy to relapse around my family.

The honesty, laughter and support in the recovery rooms helped me to cope immensely with my disease and the lack of support from some of my family. My mind raced sometimes, and my confidence could evaporate easily. I had obtained my confidence from a bottle for twenty years. I had to work at building myself back up to find some real confidence.

I was ready to trust another person properly and to accept I did not have to do it all on my own. I found a wonderful sponsor who helped me go through the rest of the twelve steps over the following year. She was an American woman living in Ireland.

She constantly told me 'Keep your side of the street clean, what anyone else thinks of you is none of your business.'

This was difficult to take on board. I had been a chameleon and a people-pleaser all my life, without even realising it. I was angry at myself for that.

I had to learn how to say 'no' to others and myself. She taught me the twelve-step programme as a way of life; a healthy, decent and happy way of being in the world.

I shifted into a less chaotic phase of my recovery I wrote about it in the hope that writing it could help me let it go. I had to learn it was okay to not be okay. That was life.

I heard at the recovery meetings that there is no pain in growth, only the resistance to it. Everyone has their ups and downs and I had to learn to ride the waves, minus the cider. I was determined to keep well.

I prayed to the angels, saints, and any friends that may know me in the spirit world. For the first time ever since he died, I asked Shane to help me with my recovery.

I cried for the loss of him and my old self. I was finally grieving for Shane. I began to feel a closer bond with him in a different sort of way. I could talk to him and felt maybe he was hearing me.

As the months went by, I was feeling more of a normal human being, whatever that is. I felt ashamed and embarrassed that I had been drunk so many times. I knew the most damage I did was to myself. I was a happy drunk in public and a sad hungover person in private.

There was talk in the recovery rooms of amends. I was at the point of making amends to others. Essentially this is where you say sorry for any hurt that was caused by your addiction even if it was unintentional. I became happier every day within myself and I wanted to clear up any mess from the past.

I had likely worried or hurt Paula over the years. I made a list in my phone for the things I wanted to apologise to her for. I asked her to meet me specifically to do this. She was back again from America for the summer.

We met on the seafront. Summer in Ireland is never without a nip in the air by the sea. My face was warm because my blood pressure was high with the nerves of it. I had been warned that people are not always kind and accepting of the amends. It was my job to apologise and understand I cannot control what happens after that.

'Hey Paula, do you want to go for a walk, or will we do this first?' I asked awkwardly.

'Sure, there is bench over there. Let's sit down first.'

I could feel my mouth going dry as we headed to the bench and sat down half facing each other and glancing out at the sea.

'Okay, I put a note on my phone so I wouldn't forget anything. I want to say sorry to you for any upset my drinking caused you.'

'Okay.' I could not tell from her tone if it actually was ok. I read through the list of ways I thought I may have hurt her.

'I'm sorry for all the nights I woke you up when we lived together, coming in noisy and drunk after a night out, for taking and losing some of your stuff, for leaving the front door unlocked, for making a show of you at weddings.'

'Okay, Lucy.'

It had not been okay. I remembered her shouting at me one night for waking her up. I had borrowed her handbag and left it in the pub. Then I turned up at the front door with a taxi man awaiting payment.

I wanted her to respond, even if it was to give out to me. My idea of fun when I was drunk had hurt her and I wanted to make amends to her. I felt she deserved that apology. The one thing I never wanted to do was hurt anyone.

It is very likely I hurt ex-boyfriends and some old friends. Never intentionally but nonetheless enough that I wanted to change. I could not tell if it was sinking in with Paula or if she was angry and did not want to unleash it on me.

I kept going, 'I'm sorry for being blacked out at the weddings we have been at together.'

She was kind of giggling. I concluded maybe she wanted to listen and not respond.

'Look, I'm sorry for all the nights out that we were on, where I was totally locked and maybe embarrassed you or you felt you had to mind me.'

She was again giggling. It was hard to tell if she was taking it seriously or not. Maybe she wanted this strange and lengthy apology to end.

I stopped. I had made enough blanket statements to cover the repeat offences. 'So that's it, as long as you know I'm sorry.'

'Ok, Lucy, will we go for the walk now?'

'Yeah, sure, thanks.'

This is how it always was with Paula: nothing ever got resolved properly because she would not discuss things with me. I was glad I said sorry. Yet because she laughed off my efforts and made no comment, it did not lend itself to any conversation or resolution.

I decided I would not be going there with others. I figured the best amends regarding everyone else was for me to be happy and well and leave those messy days behind me. Once they saw me healthy and sober, they would not have to worry.

There were the ex-boyfriends I knew I hurt. I had a bad habit of knowing I wanted to leave a relationship, then not telling the other person my doubts until we were having 'that' conversation whereby I was ending the relationship.

Alternatively, I would decide I wanted out and feel a real urgency to end things. The broken-up- with party often found out in a sudden and swift manner. That was not an intentional pattern but nonetheless it was not fair.

I broke up with one long-term boyfriend because he 'drank too much' even though he was six foot and I matched him drink for drink on nights out. The denial was that strong. They were always the problem, never me.

I knew different now and I asked my sponsor if I should make amends to them. She advised me that unless they were in my life or the opportunity arose naturally, that it was best to let those sleeping dogs lie. I could make amends by not hurting a future partner with my drinking antics.

There was one person I knew I wanted to apologise to and that was Charlie. The last thing he said to me was, 'I hope you figure out whatever it is you are running to or away from, Lucy.'

Not anymore. I was facing myself and my past. I wanted to tell Charlie I was sorry we met at the wrong time. I did not know how I would possibly explain that I had not known I was an alcoholic. I had been trying to run from myself. I was not sure if he would understand.

I wondered how I might possibly pluck up the courage to contact him and let him know I was back in Ireland. I was nervous. *What if he's moved on?*

After another couple of months, the thought entered my mind again, I wanted to contact him. I was back from America too long now; he might not appreciate the delayed sharing of this information. I felt fragile and I was not sure if I would handle it very well if he met someone else.

Perhaps as time was gone by, he would not see me through the same rose-tinted lens and think I was a fool. There it was again, Dad's voice telling me I was not good enough. I had to tell myself, *just because that idiot says it does not mean it's true.* It was hard to convince myself.

After a couple of restless nights, I made the decision to email Charlie. I was not going to be able to settle until I did something. I knew I would rather be sorry for something I did do, then did not do.

With my heart beating in my chest, I wrote him an email. It simply said, 'Hello, Charlie, how are you?' My chat function told me he was online. I obsessively re-read what I wrote to him. I immediately got a reply. *Jesus,* I thought, *he is not a figment of my imagination after all.*

He wrote 'Hi, Lucy, long time no hear. I'm good. How are you? How is American life treating you?' I took a deep breath and steadied my fingers to type, 'I'm back from America. I lasted two weeks over there.'

I braced myself for his response to that news. I was hoping Charlie was going to be happy I was in Ireland. That he was not going to be upset I had not been in America for long.

He replied, 'What?' I felt sick and quickly explained I had gone for two weeks and realised it was not for me. I had been figuring out a lot since my return. I now had a new job and a new place to live.

Charlie seemed surprised and happy I was back. He was not one to give me hassle or state the obvious that it had been a year now since my two weeks 'emigration.' We chatted online for a while.

I was getting ahead of myself, but I hoped he was single and if he was that he would be willing to give me a second chance. I was going to have to meet him to find out. I had no clue how to instigate a meet up.

I wondered, *how am I supposed to get him to ask me out again?* I knew I was being ridiculous. I did not expect him to do that. After all I was the one who finished things, disappeared and reappeared from nowhere.

I did something I had never done in my whole life. I asked him did he want to meet up with me. I always let the guys do the chasing. I knew it was up to me now. I did not want to ask him out straight if he was seeing anyone that was for him to reveal.

Hours went by and there was no reply. I went for a walk to the seafront feeling disheartened. I knew we were not going to pick up where we left off or maybe even at all. I hoped he would at least meet me.

I video called Paula that night and explained, 'If I never get Charlie back, I'll happily stay single for the rest of my life. It's him or no one.'

Paula told me to, 'Calm down and stop being so melodramatic. He will write back. Relax, Lucy.' Rightly so.

The following morning Charlie replied. He seemed in great form and he agreed to meet up. We emailed back and forth and arranged to meet on Grafton Street. I was not sure if it was a date or not. I hoped it was. Either way I was excited. I planned what I would wear and suddenly I got nervous. My hopes were already up.

The week we were due to meet up I was lying on the couch watching the soaps after work. My phone rang. It was Charlie. I could not believe it; he was phoning me. I had not expected him to ring, nor had I psyched myself up for the call.

I jumped up off the couch and backed away from the phone. Even though I was alone I was saying out loud to myself really fast, 'Oh, Jesus, Jesus, it's Charlie, he is ringing. That's brave.'

I took a breath and answered, trying to sound all calm and casual. 'Hi, Charlie, how are you?' Like it had not been one year since we spoke, or I had not been running away from and then back to the phone.

He replied in an animated tone, 'Hey, Lucy, it's so good to hear your voice.'

He sounded like he missed me. We chatted excitedly for an hour as if we had never been apart. After I got off the phone my head was in a spin. I did a little jump up and down on the spot with excitement.

By the time we met up I was back to being nervous. I was wondering, *did he actually even sound enthusiastic at all on the phone? Maybe I imagined it.*

It was a warm and sunny Sunday morning. We met outside Stephen's Green Park. Charlie looked everywhere except into my eyes, and he kept his hands in his pockets. There was no reunion hug welcome. I had never seen him this way with me.

I suggested that we go for a stroll. As we passed a pond some drunk guys were falling around being very loud and obnoxious. Charlie said, 'I hope they fall into the pond.' He sounded like he meant it.

He was not making it easy for me. I asked him about his golf and as he showed me a photo on his phone of a television, he won playing. I could smell his aftershave. It was lovely being physically close to him again.

We walked out of the park and headed down Grafton Street. It was busy and we accidentally bumped into each other as we walked along. I smiled and laughed a bit nervously.

As we neared Bewley's I braved suggesting that we go in for a coffee. He agreed and as we went in the door, we brushed off each other again. I caught him flush too. The chemistry was there. I smiled on the inside.

While he drank his coffee, and I had my hot chocolate we were forced into eye contact as we were sitting across from each other. He looked at me from underneath his eyebrows, I had missed those glances.

As soon as I saw that and the old familiar twinkle in his eye, even more of him came flooding back to me. I had forgotten the operation he had on his eye where he was given a false lens. It literally twinkled in certain lights.

I joked that his previously named 'glitter ball eye' was as 'twinkly as ever.' We talked about our lives and neither of us mentioned our time together. He dropped me home. I asked him would he like to meet again, and he agreed. We had a long goodbye hug.

That night I realised that by going to Stephen's Green and then to Bewley's on Grafton Street we had replicated our first date without intending to.

The next day at work all I thought of was Charlie. Every song was him, everything that happened I wanted to tell him. It was only a matter of weeks before it was as if we had never been apart. We hooked up at every opportunity.

One night we went to a fundraiser in a north Dublin bar near where I was living, Dan was doing a head shave for charity. All my family and some of my friends were there, except for Paula. Charlie met them all at once.

The place was packed with people and the tables were steeped in pints and bottles of cider. The music was blaring. I was fine for a while, but I was not that comfortable being around so much cider. It still looked a little attractive.

After a couple of hours, it was getting to be too much for me. I told Charlie I wanted to leave. On the way back in the car I told Charlie, 'Thanks for leaving early with me; I prefer not to be in bars for more than a couple of hours anymore.'

'Sure, it's no biggie; I'm not a major fan of it either.' I explained 'For me it's the same as a person on a diet hanging around in cake shops.'

Shane once told me that I was a typical Cancerian; the crab that goes at things sideways. I never understood what he meant until that moment. I was using a not-so-great analogy to try to get Charlie to guess that I am an alcoholic.

'Lucy, what are you trying to say? You are counting cider calories?'

'No, Charlie, you know the way I don't drink anymore?'

'Yeah?'

'Well, it's because I can't drink. Once I start drinking, I can't stop, even if I want to. I'm an alcoholic, Charlie.'

With tears rolling down my cheeks I watched closely for his reaction with my heart in my mouth. His expression was baffled. He looked as if he did not want to believe what I was telling him.

It was unfair of me to say this to him when he was driving. If I did not do it in that moment, I worried I might never have found the courage again.

He stayed silent for a minute then said, 'I'll pull in here.' Charlie took off his seat belt and shifted sideways in the seat, he looked at me lovingly and hugged me tight. 'I love you, Lucy, I'm glad you don't drink. It doesn't matter about the past. We'll not drink together, that suits me fine.'

'Are you sure? You don't think I'm a nut?'

'No, Lucy, I know you're a nut, you're my nut.'

I was now laughing and crying at the same time.

The relief was immense. Firstly, that I was not keeping it from him anymore and secondly that he was taking it so well. We sat up late talking that night and he joked that if I met him ten years earlier, he would have needed to join me at the recovery meetings.

Over the following year Charlie told me regularly how proud he was of me. I learned that the disease of untreated alcoholism is progressive but so too is the recovery.

Every month that went by I was happier and stronger. I let go of two of the huskies: Anger and Anxiety. Sadness stayed but I manged to keep it under control. I walked it now and knew what to do to keep it in perspective. It was an old companion that I tolerated. Thankfully I did not see it daily anymore.

10

Charlie and I were either in each other's places, on dates or out in nature. We had road trips around Ireland together. He tried to claim he was allergic to cats. He said that if he touched my cat Rosie he would break out in a rash. I teased him about his made-up allergy. I think he had convinced himself of it.

We both commuted a lot to work and to see each other so it made sense to move in together. We agreed to make his house our home. Charlie even became a fan of Rosie, so he let her move in too.

My high energy levels were back, but the mornings were a big struggle for me. As soon as I woke my inner voice told me, *Lucy, you are crap. Who you are fooling? You are no good. Why are you even bothering with all this stuff? It's not going to change you.*

I felt groggy; my brain was still detoxing during the nights. I was angry at myself for being such a fool. There it was: Dad's words tormenting me again *you fool, who do you think you are?*

They say a parent's voice to a child growing up becomes the child's monologue. I was told so often growing up to 'get off the stage, fool' and 'don't get above your station' or 'I'll give you a smack in the chops.'

Now here I was all these years later as an adult and I was literally afraid to get on the stage of life, to be seen and heard.

I doubted if I was good enough for Charlie. I told myself, *he will probably leave me for someone else.* Yet the difference was I felt I deserved to be happy. I was damned if I was going to let the negative voice in my head continue to convince me I was no good.

I got up in the mornings earlier than Charlie, ate breakfast, and showered while saying prayers and mantras. By the time he woke up I felt human and not as much of a grumpy troll.

While I got ready Charlie often arrived with a giant mug that he made for me, full of hot tea. It was big enough to hold two cups of tea and he called it my 'double gulp.' He will never know how much his love and that caffeine comforted me in those early days. He loved and accepted me as I was, without question, until I could.

I kept going to meetings to undo the knots life had tied me up in over the years. I learned how to not get tied up in the first place.

I convinced Charlie to adopt a King Charles Spaniel Puppy, Lolly, with me. We had a great laugh carrying out peacekeeping between Rosie and Lolly. She had been abused through dog fighting and was a nervous small scruffy thing. Charlie teased me that I was a sucker for a sob story, but he loved that dog. She followed him everywhere.

Together we loved her back to health. For her first year with us she sat by my side being snuggled and showed me a lot of love too. We practiced being parents on the cat and the dog. We both wanted children sooner rather than later and of course together.

After six months living together, I came home to find Charlie standing at the front door. He smiled as he took the Chinese take away bag out of my hand. He put an eye mask on me and led me into our sitting room.

When he removed it, there were candles everywhere. The room was warm, and the smell of orange, chocolate, and vanilla was beautiful. They had been lighting for probably an hour while he waited for me to get there. The television was playing a slideshow of photos of our times together since we met.

He was playing Leonard Cohen's song *Dance Me to the End of Love*. Charlie sat me down on the armchair and he got down on his knee in front of me. I could see he was nervous, and he had tears in his eyes. 'Lucy, you make me the happiest man alive. Will you marry me?'

I smiled with happy tears rolling down my cheeks, 'Yes, of course.'

We slow danced in our sitting room. *Dance me to the wedding now. Dance me on and on. Dance me to the children who are asking to be born.*

I was dancing, my heart was dancing, and I was the happiest I had ever been in my life. The ring was gorgeous, a sparkling diamond with smaller diamonds on each side of it on the band.

We went to look at a hotel the next day and booked it for five months later. Initially I wanted a tiny wedding on a beach, the two of us with a witness. Charlie convinced me to have close family and friends there.

Once the word was out it snowballed. Before I knew it, Hilary and Brona were bridesmaids. I had two of the cutest flower girls ever and an absolutely beautiful dress. I was so pleased that we were having our lovely wedding in Ireland after all.

My family had a good reaction to our news. That was until Kerry had a get together for us at her house and started calling it our 'Very short engagement' and asking me 'What are you *doing*?'

I honestly was stumped and asked her back, 'What do you mean?'

'Lucy, five months is *such* a short time and getting married in November just before *Christmas*?'

At this point we were in front of all of the family. 'Don't worry; all you have to do is turn up, Kerry. We will be looking after everything.'

'No actually, Lucy, I'll have to arrange outfits for my kids the month before Christmas.'

'But surely they can wear their Christmas clothes?' I wanted to tell her to *go fuck* herself.

Paula had mentioned to me after I moved in with Charlie that 'Kerry seems to be taking all of your life choices personally.' I did not really know what she meant until that moment. It seemed like lunacy to me.

People shuffled out of the kitchen until it was the two of us and Paula. Kerry stood leaning on the kitchen radiator with Paula standing beside her. I was on the opposite side of the room, literally cornered.

I asked her, 'What is your problem?' This was a mistake. She started shouting at me, 'So you want to know what *my* problem is? I've to dress four kids, book a hotel, and it's not a matter of just turning up Lucy.'

I looked from her to Paula wide-eyed with shock. Paula said nothing. I was so hurt and disappointed. I knew what Kerry's problem was, I was no longer allowing her to control me, and she could not stand it. Kerry snarled at me, 'And now you are crying like a four-year-old.'

This attack was at an engagement meal she arranged for me. She gave me one day's notice and she had it at a time she knew I could not make. I told her I was coming from work. She went ahead and had the meal without us.

I left crying with Charlie and hoped he was not already regretting marrying into such madness. Despite the family drama, I enjoyed the build-up to the wedding as much as possible.

Brona and Hilary organised a hen party for me. It was a meal in the Japanese restaurant. They presented me with a lovely box. Inside there was an envelope from each friend with a note on the outside and photos of them and me over the years inside. I still have that box and I treasure it.

Sissy was her fabulous self that night, downing red wine and making it look so attractive. My sponsor became a friend of mine and she came to the hen, too. At one stage she leaned over the table to me and said, 'Sissy even makes me want to drink.'

I laughed. She had noticed I was having what they call in addiction recovery 'euphoric recall.' This is when you remember all the fun you had in active addiction. The singing, the dancing, the laughing, the confidence, the feeling attractive and loving yourself and everyone else.

I needed to 'play the tape forward' as my sponsor had imparted repeatedly. I had to remember the anxiety, the depression, and the self-loathing and wanting to die.

That was enough to snap me out of any notions that might cross my mind. I am an alcoholic; it is natural for me to want to have a drink. I have to quash that thought like a vicious virus before it spreads in my mind.

We had a great night. Kerry parked herself at the furthest end of the table. Her expression said she did not want to be there. Of course, Mam sat with her. It hurt me feeling no warmth from them around this time. It seemed like my punishment for having a short engagement.

Brona phoned me the night before the wedding. We got reminiscing about my relationships over the years. The two of us laughed that when we were children, we asked our neighbour Christopher, the love we found on my road, to pick one of us to be his girlfriend.

He had to let us know his decision by writing one of our initials, either the letter L for Lucy or B for Brona in the big pile of sand outside the Bank of Ireland beside his house.

When D-day came for Christopher, the one we loved, to declare who the chosen girl was, we were nervous and excited. All we knew was he was thinking about it.

While we awaited his verdict, we wrote in huge capital letters 'I love YOU by you know HOW' on the wall beside his house. Brona's spelling was as brutal as mine.

As we walked by after school his mother threatened that if we did not wash it off, she would tell our parents. We scrubbed it with water and washing up liquid, but because we used crayons on the white gloss painted wall it would not budge.

I lived in fear of her telling my parents, especially Dad. I refused to walk that way home from school. I did not want anyone else to find out. Brona managed to laugh it off.

We laughed about how much devilment we got up to over the years, stealing drink and going into underage clubs. We joked that we hoped our children would not be as badly behaved as us.

We arranged for Brona to come over to my house early the next morning. Charlie was already gone to the venue the night before. We were having the civil ceremony in a beautiful small family-run hotel.

That morning I got ready at home with Hilary and Brona. Mam and my sisters arrived. I had organised for them to get their makeup done by a make-up artist too. She did mine first and I went upstairs to finish off getting ready.

When it was the moment to put on my dress, I was so excited I whipped off my dressing gown and did a little dance. I forgot I only had knickers on. There was a bra built into the dress. The two of them laughed loudly and Brona shouted, 'Charlie is one lucky man.'

When I realised I was half naked I was too giddy and happy to even care. I had my dress on at last. Hilary told me 'You look absolutely gorgeous Lucy, like an English rose.'

I am not sure what one of them looks like. All I know was I felt beautiful.

I came downstairs to do my big reveal as the bride. I was all ready to go meet my husband-to-be. I was waiting for some smiles and love and luck as every bride does in that moment. The photographer waited to snap the special interactions.

Instead, Mam approached me asking me to pay for her makeup. I had to walk away and rise above her selfishness. I went to Paula and asked her to figure it out with Mam.

The only thing Mam asked me in the whole run up to the wedding was, 'What is for dinner?' I think a stranger on the street probably had more interest in our wedding than her.

Despite Mam's narcissistic behaviour and lack of affection towards me, I parked it and had a laugh on the way to the hotel with my bridesmaids. Brona and Hilary were excited for me and Charlie and they both looked stunning. I did not care that it was a misty November day. We were in the beautiful car Charlie booked for us as a surprise.

I arrived in my stunning ivory satin wedding dress. The top half was a fitted bodice, covered with lace and lace straps and had Swarovski crystals all over it.

I chose turquoise velvet shoes that peeped out from under the dress. Before I walked in Brona reassured me, 'you look a million dollars in that dress Lucy, the shoes are gorgeous, just so you.'

My niece and Charlie's niece were dressed in little flower girls' ivory dresses with turquoise shoes too. Brona and Hilary chose gorgeous long navy dresses; the colour complemented their both being blonde.

The civil ceremony was intimate. We chose all the readings and music. Charlie's friends, two accomplished singer-song-writers, played the music for the ceremony on a keyboard and a fiddle.

Charlie smiled as I walked towards him to Nick Cave's 'Into My Arms'. We beamed at each other. I thought Charlie looked the most handsome I ever saw him. He is one of those men who is lovely looking but does not know it.

He was wearing a fitted navy-blue Italian suit, with a crisp ivory shirt and a blue tie with tiny turquoise flowers on it. He had a white rose as his buttonhole to match my bouquet.

He picked everything himself, with characteristics akin to a Groomzilla which entertained me greatly. It was not what I would have expected from him. It was great that he gave so much attention to all the details and he was brilliant at it all.

His smile was the biggest I had ever seen, and we did not stop smiling at each other. We actually giggled on and off throughout the ceremony. I think it was a mix of nerves, excitement, and relief.

I was incredibly nervous on the morning of the wedding. I even went for a walk along the canal to try to expend some nervous energy.

Once I was by his side at the ceremony, I felt relaxed and happy. His two groomsmen were by his other side. One was his long-standing workmate and the other was one of the musicians, who he was also friends with for many years. Two absolute top guys full of character and respect, the same as my Charlie.

They chose to wear their own suits one in a tweed brown and the other in black. I liked that it added a slightly alternative look to the wedding party, and they looked brilliant. It also helped disguise the fact that I did not make Dad part of the wedding party, by buying him a suit or by giving him a buttonhole flower like the rest of the men.

I let him walk me up the aisle to avoid conflict, from Kerry mostly. I made up my mind before then that as I walked away from him to Charlie that I would create an invisible line and I would sever that line. I knew I would never let Dad be so close to me ever again, in any sense.

Once all the proceedings got going, we forgot there was anyone else there other than the celebrant. I just wanted to be married to Charlie. It was not until after we had done the 'I do's' and we were signing the register that I looked up and saw all the faces behind phones photographing us.

We both smiled back at our guests as a blushing bride and

groom. It was an extremely proud and happy moment. When all that was done and the celebrant said,

'You may kiss the bride.' Charlie's friends played us down the aisle to one of their own feel-good songs called 'For a Cat', *Love finds us all, who cares where you're at. I was climbing the walls when you're crazy, took my crazy, for a cat.*

I was busy chatting to all our guests. Aunty Clare brought a silver boot with a blue ribbon on it, and we were photographed with her and it. It was sweet that she wanted to give me something old and blue.

It was a unique day, where you talk to everyone and no one. We snuck off to the room as soon as we got a chance and ate the chocolates that awaited us.

We entered the reception as husband and wife to the Beatles singing *All You Need is Love*. Charlie did a lovely speech. He joked, making a reference to my favourite film where Jack Nicholson says, 'You make me want to be a better man.'

If I was not so shy about public speaking, I would have said you are the best man I could ever know. I told him later. The rest of the wedding was the usual eating of a good meal, followed by dessert and the cutting of the cake. We loved that part.

Charlie's mam made us a gorgeous chocolate biscuit cake with white icing and turquoise decorations on it. As we cut it, we had a big chomp on it too. We both gave up carbohydrates in the run up to the wedding. We made up for it.

Our first dance was to the song Charlie played as he proposed. It was special to us. Dad's speech said some good things: 'Oh we were very proud that she got a medal from Trinity.'

Charlie's friend shouted out, 'If she's that clever, what's she doing marrying him?'

I felt embarrassed that Dad sounded like he was bragging. I was delighted that Charlie's friend distracted everyone. Dad added, 'Charlie, if she ever gets in a mood, ignore her and she will come around.'

Charlie smiled politely but I knew he was thinking the same as me: *go fuck yourself.*

Once we left my house that morning Kerry barely spoke to me all day. At one stage I motioned with my hand for her to come and join me at a table with Paula, who had a big baby bump, and was sitting beside me. She shook her head no.

Paula shared a room with Kerry and her family. I did not feel that close to her on that day either. She wanted to surprise me for the wedding. In the run up to the wedding I was crying because Paula would not be there. To cheer me up Charlie told me in advance that she was coming.

I told Paula on a video call, that I knew, and I was so excited she was coming. Paula did not take it well, she swiftly ended the call and refused to talk to me between then and arriving in Ireland just before the wedding.

Kerry got involved telling Charlie he should have let me cry. Charlie now appeared to be in the bad books with both of my sisters. We hoped they would come around before the wedding, but they still appeared not to be able to be very happy for us.

There were twenty nieces and nephews running around, which for me always adds to a wedding. Children are the best fun and dance like nobody is watching. There were dance-offs. The children always won.

Dan got drunk and fell asleep at midnight for the night. I missed his fun around the place that night. I danced my socks off with Charlie and my friends.

Brona and Hilary and their husbands all got drunk and were great fun. Sissy, my friends from school, college, work and Earthsong were all there and in great form, they made the day for me.

Before the music ended, Kerry disappeared up to her room. When the dancing was over, we all went into the bar. Charlie and I talked and laughed with relatives.

Now I was off the dance floor, my drunk aunty, the 'golden alcoholic' as Mam liked to call her took the opportunity to come up to me. According to Mam if you can function, despite drinking copious amounts of vodka, you are one of them.

The 'golden' one informed me Mam was disappointed she had to pay for her own make-up that morning. I wanted to tell her to *mind your own bloody business* and to ask her *was that the only thing my mother had to say about the day?* I already knew the answer to that.

I brushed her bullshit off and walked away. Charlie and I had a good time and said our good nights, with lots of hugs and kisses from our lovely guests.

Brona told me the next day that after Charlie and I went to bed Kerry re-joined the group in the bar. Regardless of my family of origin and their antics, Charlie and I had a beautiful wedding with our friends.

Nothing took from our happiness at being newly married. We sat up, talking and eating chocolate again. Charlie had a task to take all the sparking crystal flowers out of my hair. I did not want to take off my dress that night. I have never loved a dress so much in my life.

We talked about how we loved the day and sharing it with our guests. It was a fancy portal to us into the real deal of being husband and wife, the marriage, and committing to being our best selves for each other.

The following morning, we were not afraid to admit to each other that we could not wait to get away alone for the weekend to relax and absorb our wonderful day.

Charlie and I are alike in that we are both introverts who love being around people. We can disguise ourselves well as extroverts but then we need to rest.

We sat in the lobby and chatted to everyone. Some of my uncles were making their inappropriate 'jokes' to one of my friends, about her pregnancy so I found an excuse to get away.

I went to ask the hotel staff to wrap up some chunks of our wedding cake to give to Mam and Kerry. I was informed by the staff that they had already requested and obtained them.

Brona and I sat with them and Kerry suggested I leave my bouquets behind to be placed on Shane's grave. This felt a bit sad and morbid to me. I never heard of this kind of tradition. I did not want my bouquet to be wilting away in a graveyard. When I hesitated, Brona jumped in and said she would leave hers. I felt I should too, so I did.

Charlie and I had a red lantern on the table at our ceremony. We asked the celebrant to announce that we were 'lighting a candle in this lantern for all Charlie and Lucy's relatives who have passed away and cannot be here today. Especially for Lucy's brother Shane.'

We had a beautiful instrumental piece of music playing from one of Charlie's friend's original songs that we love. I fought back the tears; it was an emotional moment.

I had one of those long skinny candles that are used to light another candle. My hand was shaking so much that I was not able to light the candle in the lantern. I also could not bend because the bodice of the dress was so tight. Charlie put his hand on mine to steady it and the candle lit.

I asked Paula to take the lantern into the main reception for the evening too and she did. I had a real sense of Shane actually standing behind us at the ceremony. I imagine he was dancing in the circle with us that night.

That was our nod of respect and inclusion to Shane and anyone else who had passed away or missing from our wedding. Kerry always had a way of making me feel like I was not doing things right or good enough.

I did not bother mentioning it to Charlie; it cannot be easy for him getting the raw deal with his in-laws.

I found Brona and Hilary and we laughed at the state of them the night before. We said our goodbyes before we headed to stay in the beautiful lodge on a lake for a couple of days.

They gave us the best room in the place. It was huge and overlooking the lake. I put all the wedding cards up in the room and I felt loved by Charlie. Even though it was November I remember it almost as if it was summer. We were so bright and beaming. It did not matter what time of year it was in our bubble that weekend.

We went back to work for a few weeks before we had time off at Christmas for the honeymoon. We did not mind; we were still on a high for those weeks.

A month later just before Christmas, Charlie and I flew off on our honeymoon to Abu Dhabi. On the plane I had some cramping pains, but I was not due my period yet. I hoped it was not coming randomly on our honeymoon.

It crossed my mind I might be pregnant. We had stopped using contraception since the wedding. It had not been the window in the month for pregnancy to occur, so I dismissed the notion.

Before we left, as a joke, Charlie put a pregnancy test in my suitcase and said it was part of my Christmas stocking. We agreed to decide on honeymoon if we would start to try for a baby then or if we would wait six months.

Upon arrival we were chauffeured to the five-star hotel. Neither of us had ever seen the opulence and utter glamour that awaited us. From the high ceilings to the marble floors reflecting a gigantic Christmas tree it was spectacular. Everything was so pristine, sparkling in the heat.

In the hotel lobby, tour operators were giving out lots of information on all the activities to do while there. We had already booked to go on a safari, so we gave them a swerve. The room was super swanky too. We were chuffed with ourselves and went straight for a long nap.

I woke up after about four hours. Charlie was still fast asleep. I needed to pee. I had a vague recollection of reading on the pregnancy test pack that it was best to take it with the first pee of the day. Before I knew it, I was compelled to take the test.

I had been feeling bloated, but I was convinced it was my imagination. I did the test and while I waited, I thought how Charlie would think I was utterly mad. We were not even trying for baby yet.

We had literally arrived on our honeymoon. I could justify taking it to rule out a pregnancy before the safari. I hoped Charlie would laugh that I used the test already.

I waited the couple of minutes and then glanced at it to confirm I was not pregnant, and we would be going on the safari.

I looked at the test there were two blue lines. It was positive. Every cell in my body reacted with joy. I waved my arms in the air, utterly overjoyed. I ran out and jumped on the bed beside Charlie, waking him and telling him he was going to be a dad.

He was speechless and half asleep. We could not believe it. We were going to have a baby. I cried with happiness. We had no idea that we had brought a bundle of joy on honeymoon with us. I did not stop smiling.

Our first dance song had predicted it. Leonard Cohen was right, *Dance me on and on, dance me to the children asking to be born.*

11

The first person we told was the tour guide. He advised us we could do a safari minus the sand dune jeep ride or the camel ride. We would see the desert and sleep in a romantic hut. We loaded up our back packs. I smiled inside that Charlie's face was so full of excitement.

We were picked up at our hotel by two very serious guides and we were off. There were new stops included on the trip. We were going to a temple and a market. Along the way we broke into hysterics over very little.

At the temple at one point a frenzied security guard appeared out of nowhere. He had a gun and insisted an inch of my shoulder was indecently exposed and therefore visible to him. My cardigan had slipped sideways.

In a low voice I said to Charlie, 'Seriously. What. The. Fuck?' As I quickly covered myself up.

'Your sinful shoulder is causing a stir.' He tried to help me laugh it off, but he spoke slightly nervously now. I was annoyed at the absolute ridiculousness of it. I did not dare challenge the security guard.

At the market, Charlie bought me a beautiful gold necklace. It was half of a butterfly with a red ruby stone on its wing. I was already dreaming of giving it to my baby if it was a girl.

We drove for ages along the sand and eventually met with some other tourists for dinner. After stuffing ourselves with a barbeque and bashfully becoming part of belly dancer show, we were spent. We were looking forward to being alone later.

My biggest dilemma was that I needed to pee, badly. It had been a decent drive to the barbeque area. We guessed it might be an even longer drive to our overnight accommodation.

As I attempted to sneak off into the dunes one of the tour guides called me back. 'You're going the wrong way. The jeep is that way. We've one last stop for you two: star gazing for the honeymooners.'

When we got to the star-gazing spot I was exhausted and thought I might wet myself. I could not face the mortification. They laid out a blanket for us 'Sit, relax, and look at the stars for half an hour, then we'll be going again.'

'Okay, thanks,' we replied in unison.

The guides headed back to sit in the jeep, which was facing the other direction. As I lay on Charlie's shoulder, I drifted off to sleep, aware that I needed to pee. I thought I could perhaps nip away out of sight as we were among sand dunes.

I was not sure if I was awake or asleep. I told Charlie, 'I will be super quick; they won't even know I'm gone.'

Before I ran off, I pecked Charlie on the cheek and squeezed his arm. He smiled and pulled me back close, whispering, 'Hurry up you.'

'Of course, love,' I whispered back.

I am afraid of the dark, but I ran straight into the dunes. I remembered the guard with the gun at the temple and for fear of it being illegal to pee in public I sprinted a bit further into the dunes.

When I was done, I ran back towards Charlie and the guides, scared in the pitch black. I was nervous they would have copped what I was doing and there might be consequences. I was running fast. I did not realise I had run so far away from Charlie. It occurred to me I must have turned myself around and ran away from them. So, I ran in a different direction.

I have what I call 'directions dyslexia,' anyone else who has this will identify with how tricky it can be. I have been shopping on a Grafton Street in Dublin all my life and I can come out of a shop and not remember from which direction I came. I can walk back in the same direction and realise I have already been that way. That is with years of familiarity and streetlights.

It was pitch dark and only the stars distinguished the sky from the ground. My heart was pounding in my chest. I ran again, a third time in a different direction, thinking it must be this way. Then I ran again in another direction, further. I was thinking it must be that way.

I went to get my phone from my pocket and realised I left it in Charlie's backpack. I panicked. I was now running further and faster. I was afraid to shout out to Charlie to locate him in case they heard me, and I got us into trouble for leaving. I knew they had some serious rules for women there.

I called out to Charlie in my mind *Look for me, please. Come find me, Charlie. Please I need your help, Charlie.* I had been lost before abroad and I found my way, like when I followed the guy with the yellow backpack in Thailand. I reminded myself of that.

I took deep breaths and held back the tears. I did not want to overreact. I told myself repeatedly, *I've been lost before. I'll find my way.* I felt panic like this in Bangkok and that all worked out fine. This would too. It had to.

I continued to run over and back in different directions. The fear took over and I realised I had to risk the consequences and called out, 'Charlie, Charlie, Charlie, Charlie, Charlieee.'

I was convinced I would hear him call back to me, but nothing. Not a sound. I did some panicked praying. That was all that kept the hyperventilation at bay. I shouted out again, 'Over here, Charlie. I'm over hereee.'

I kept walking in the same direction. I remembered that I heard somewhere before that all paths lead to a road. It was more like tall and flat bumps than a path. I misjudged that and fell over repeatedly.

I was running out of steam, so I alternated between walking and running. I walked and I ran again and again until I was spent. I could not believe what was happening asking myself *is it possible I'm lost in the desert on my honeymoon? Alone.*

I was crying and panicking now. Nothing helped to calm me. It was too dark, and I was too alone. I kept walking and falling over from exhaustion, crying onto the sand.

At some point I must have passed out. I woke early with the sun rising and my mouth felt like dry mud. I wracked my brain for any tips I may have heard on how to find your way or be found in a desert.

I kept walking, adrenaline and fear kept me going for hours and hours, until I passed out again. I was alternating between despair and exhaustion-induced apathy. The heat was draining me too. I felt my face burning.

This happened over and over. I am not sure for how long. It went on until I caught sight of something in the distance.

My legs gathered momentum. An unexpected burst of energy soared through my body and I ran over to a hut.

I wondered if this was our honeymoon hut, except Charlie was not there waiting for me. Instead, I saw a dusty mound stretched out on the porch of the sun-bleached hut. If this was the love nest for Charlie and me, it was now apparently policed by an old tiger.

I found a level of either courage or stupidity I never knew I had because I silently slipped off my trekking boots and tiptoed past him into the hut. I held my breath while I opened the door. It was a simple latch to lift. I shook as I gently lifted it.

Once inside, I quietly, with my heart beating in my ears, emptied a cabinet full of books and inch by inch I pushed it in front of the door. Then I replaced all the books. Maybe that would keep me safe until the tiger was gone.

I took tiny steps towards the window and held my breath as I looked out. He was asleep and looked fairly ragged and old with an enormous head.

There were no neighbouring huts. Mine was one big room and a bathroom; it had two hammocks hanging by a window and a double bed with two towels on it. They were folded into swans with a note saying, 'Welcome Lucy and Charlie.'

I was too much in survival mode for it to register the absurd situation I was finding myself in. I thought to myself, *Okay, Lucy, so you are being held hostage by a tiger in a hut on your honeymoon, pregnant and minus a husband.* It was so ridiculous I could not believe it. I willed Charlie to turn up and I was convinced he would.

There was a small fridge and to my delight there was bottled water in it. There was a working tap, some fresh food, dried and canned food and lots of fruit to keep us going for our self-catering stay.

I told myself, *so worst-case scenario there is enough for one month for me and the baby.* I relaxed a tiny bit; *there is no way I'll be here for a month so at least we will not be dying from starvation.*

The stock included packets of biscuits and some cakes. I guzzled a bottle of water and scavenged two biscuits. My forming baby was hungry. My lips cracked as I ate, and I was nearly choking on them as my throat was so dry.

As the water hit my stomach, I felt queasy. I was in the middle of heaving when I saw something behind me out of the corner of my eye. I turned to see the back door was slightly open. I was a foot away from it.

Then he appeared in the doorway. The tiger. He was turning slowly and silently to face me. Oh, he was curious now, awake and on all fours. His head was even more enormous than I initially thought. He suddenly became real and dangerous.

A very serious voice in my head warned me *this is no harmless old dusty cat; this is an agile animal. Look at the wiry hair standing up along his spine.*

I never experienced the flight or fight mechanism kick in so strong until that moment. I belted towards the door at an inhuman speed, and I kicked it closed. There was a key in it. I locked it with the highest speed imaginable.

There was a loud bang from the other side, then another and another. My heart was pounding. I was not sure if it was his head or his tail hitting the door.

I remembered hearing tigers sneak up on their prey, biting the back of their neck or head. That must have been what he had been trying to do. I sat on the floor trying to calm myself down.

I named him Ted. Possibly this was in an attempt to convince myself he was tamer than I feared. Ted is typically a nice guy name, the kind of guy everybody likes.

For now, I was quietly confident Ted was not able to lift a latch and push past a case full of books or turn a key. He had claws but I had fingers. Although he did have massive teeth, we both had our strong suits.

There was a large glass panel in the back door. This unnerved me as I feared he might try to come crashing through it. The panel was roughly halfway up the door. I imagined him jumping that high no problem.

I felt safer staying down low on the floor. If I was out of sight my visual presence would not taunt him to try to crash through the glass panel. I hoped.

Every now and then I moved around in tiny steps very slowly investigating the hut. I was hoping I would make some discovery as to how to escape safely. I found nothing. I sat down frozen on the floor wondering *what the fuck am I going to do.*

When I finally plucked up the courage to stand up again and look out the window, I saw him. He had resumed the same lying down position I had initially discovered him in. He was at the back door again. I tiptoed closer to the large glass panel on the door. I clocked his huge tail, half the length of his body. It looked powerful. I felt that alone would certainly knock me out.

There was no curtain on that window. The other main window had some. I silently and slowly took the rail down and removed the curtains. I managed to stand on a chair and take two wall plates down from above the door. I hung one of the curtains over the back door and the glass panel.

I was worn out from trying to be so silent and stealthy. Once I finished, I crouched on the floor, crying and frustrated. Now I could not see him, but I knew he was there. I kept the curtain rail with me, my weapon of defence should I need to use it against my captor.

I got to know the sounds of Ted. His claws at the front door. His heavy breathing emanating from his hairy face under the back door. Often if I was near the back door, I smelt his foul breath while he sniffed at the tiny gap between the door and the floor.

I have a good sense of smell, but pregnancy was making it sensitive to the point of superhuman smelling powers. Any smells pleasant or unpleasant were causing me to feel nauseous.

It triggered me back to all those hangovers and that induced wild levels of anxiety in me. I thought my days of feeling anxious and alone were behind me. I cried and cried inside the hut.

I tried to wrap myself up in the hammock. Bar moving the curtains, for the first few days I was too scared to do any unnecessary movements inside of the hut. Let alone attempt to go outside.

I did not think us humans were top of a tiger's menu, but pickings were likely sparse in a desert. This guy was getting old. Maybe he might fancy a rag doll to throw around with his jaws.

I knew if tigers are old or injured, they might turn to humans. My tiny forming baby and I were easy prey. The thought made me crumple again into a mess of tears and snot. *How is this happening to me?*

I went from being the happiest I had ever been in my life to being the most scared I had ever been. I felt completely lost. I can always find a solution in any situation and focus on it. I was even professionally trained to do so. I did not know what to do, which caused me to despair.

I thought of Charlie constantly. I hoped he would rescue me. He was the most loving and courageous person I knew. He would take a bullet for me. I knew he would certainly do his best to find me.

I tried to think what Charlie would do. I wished and willed for him to be in the other hammock beside me. I wanted him to somehow know the urgency of how much his baby was in danger. I needed him to go ahead and get hysterical right now and come and find us.

I could not take being stuck in a hot hut. Feeling like I might be attacked at any moment. I was sending him tele-pathic messages, holding back the hysteria myself while willing Charlie to worry for me.

I noted Ted's patterns of sleep. When he wandered away from the hut. I hoped he was hunting successfully and not hungry. He left the porch late most evenings once it got dark. I was never sure if he was gone hunting or for a wander.

I did not risk opening the door in case he had returned unannounced and was looming, waiting to pounce. It reminded me of sneaking around the house as a child, afraid if Dad woke up, I would incur his wrath.

I did not think I would survive a tussle with a tiger. Even an old smelly one and there was no way I was going to risk my baby being hurt.

I knew for sure he had strayed off hunting when I heard him chewing on whatever he had dragged back. Often it was a goat-type coat with antlers and black hair that he would devour, nothing too big.

I feared he was constantly hungry. I was too. It was probably the pregnancy increasing my appetite. I always envisaged myself to eat healthily during pregnancy and to be taking vitamins. Instead, here I was rationing the food that was left for the honeymooners.

Honeymooner does not have the same ring to it. I had been there two weeks now, so my rations were dwindling. I had to be careful not to leave myself without food.

It was Groundhog Day watching, waiting, and praying for a solution or to be found. I talked to my tiny forming baby a lot and reassured the baby everything would be ok and not to worry. I tried to convince myself too.

My stomach regularly rumbled, and I shook with low blood sugar. Most days I did not move much so that did not help either. I was in constant fear of drawing attention to myself.

Occasionally when the stomach-ache got too much, I gently tiptoed around while he was asleep taking a bite to eat. The hunger reared up and I savaged the nearest foods I found. Afterwards I often felt sick with indigestion. I suspected I had a shrinking stomach internally. I was worried my baby bump was almost getting flatter instead of rounder. I knew I had to nourish my baby, so I did my best.

I ran out of bottled water and prayed the running water I was drinking was not causing my baby any harm. My mind constantly flitted between telling me, *the baby is fine. It has no idea any of this is going on; it's a ball of cells right now.* To, *oh, Christ, this baby is going to be ruined on every level from all this stress.* I knew the situation was not good for the baby. I became obsessed with finding a way back to my lovely life.

One afternoon Ted left unexpectedly. He was heading off by day for a change. I watched him stride along his usual trail. I waited for a few long moments then I spontaneously said a God help me prayer and I attempted to leave too.

As soon as I put my foot outside the door he reappeared. He was around the back of the hut. He soared back into sight, leaping at me. The speed was incredible. He flew at least ten metres in the same time it took me to turn around and take one step back into the hut. I managed to bang the door shut and lock it in a half a second.

It took me a moment to realise he had sliced the back of my leg with the tip of his claws. I was so full of adrenaline I had not even felt it. I noticed blood rolling down my leg onto my boots and onto the wooden floor. I cleaned myself up.

Thankfully I only took one step out the door. Even one step more and I was most definitely a goner. I felt like there was no hope of anything anymore. This was a new low for me, even in the depths of grief or early detox and recovery I always had hope. I had nothing to cling on to.

I was failing my baby and it was not even born yet. I had no idea what I was going to do to get out of there or what Charlie or anyone back home was thinking. *Do they think I'm* missing because I have been abducted? Is Charlie looking for me in this area or somewhere else now? Why have they not come to the hut? Or did they come that night while I was lost elsewhere?

There was no way they would be thinking I was being held prisoner by a *fucking tiger*. I doubted that was on anyone's radar. I despaired, crying until I could not breathe some nights.

I noticed Ted's pattern changed. He continued to roam during the day. I wondered did he have tiger dementia. Maybe he was catching such small meat supplies by night he had to resort to day-time desert shopping.

While he went hunting, with my heart in my mouth I got closer to the back door and pressed my face up against the glass panel. I could track the direction he went off in by his footprints and fantasised I could make a run for it the other way.

I would crumple on the floor crying or thump the counter with my fists in rage and frustration until my back hurt. The fear, the anger, the isolation was too much. Sometimes I even screamed.

Occasionally the screaming was loud, and I got so angry that it got to the point I was not even sure if Ted was on the porch or not but I would continue to scream and shout. I was not sure if I was trying to scare him or to will him to come in and finish me off altogether.

When I calmed down, I panicked and felt guilty for my reckless behaviour. I was endangering myself and my baby. This was no good for either of us. I wondered if I was losing my mind, was any of this happening at all. Maybe I was in a dream or I had experienced a nervous breakdown.

I had to live for my beautiful baby. I hoped and prayed to God and Buddha and all my friends in the spirit world that my precious baby was ok. I covered all my bases, emergency praying daily and imploring Shane to help me.

On extremely warm days I think my elevated temperature caused me to slip into a type of delirium. I hallucinated and had imaginary conversations with animals that appeared at the windows.

One day the cutest grey squirrel came to me and said in an Irish accent, 'Lucy. Let's sing together.'

We sang Bob Marley's 'Three Little Birds', *Don't worry, about a thing, cause every little thing is gonna be alright.*

The squirrel and I danced, and I watched it jet around the hut for a number of hours before I came to in the delirium, singing 'Three Little Birds' with a grey Irish squirrel in Abu Dhabi. I was crying and then laughing.

I continued to talk to my friends in the spirit world repeatedly begging them to help me. I asked the angels, the saints, Shane and anyone who was listening to help Charlie to find me or to help me find some sort of solution. I prayed to keep my baby safe and preserve my sanity while I figured a way out.

I saw things that were not there, stunning meerkats appeared at the windows of the hut too. Their eyes offered me their serenity and peace. I convinced myself the hut was filling up with snakes too. It was horrendous.

I had to do something. I was now obsessed with Ted, watching his every move. I talked to him under the door. Insanely I was thinking if I befriended him and forgave the stress, the being held hostage and sliced up leg it might improve my chances.

I pleaded with him to let us go. All he had to do was disappear for a while and let me get back to being with the people I loved. I convinced myself he might let us walk away, unharmed.

After our chat, Ted appeared to have brought back something he caught and killed. It was akin to a beautiful young deer in his jaws. His beard was full of blood. I knew I had to hold off on the being friend's routine. There would be no slipping into Stockholm syndrome for me, oh no, no way.

Ted could kill me in an instant. Yet I might go mad waiting and wondering how to get free of him. Something had to relent. I prayed for an escape.

The following day I waited again until I saw Ted was gone. I waited hours to make sure he was gone far away. I edged to the back door in my newfound silent shuffle. To my delight he was not there.

I turned the key millimetre by millimetre so as not to make any noise in case I was mistaken. I took a step outside the back door. This was proving to be more promising than my previous attempt to escape.

I took the second step and I saw Ted, we made eye contact. As he leaped forwards, I darted backwards. I landed on my arse and booted the door shut. I do not remember how I was instantly back on my feet locking the door, but I was. Determination to live was giving me superpowers.

I looked down. There was blood all over the front of my trekking boot. Ted had sliced the front of my thigh open. His claw had gone in deeper this time. We had looked into each other's eyes that is how close we came. He had outstretched his claw and caught me with the bare edge end of it.

Christ, I suddenly felt the pain. It stung like crazy. I ripped up the hammock and shakily tied it around my leg. I figured I needed stiches but there was no hope of that. I craned my neck to look through the window. I had waited so long to make sure he was gone far enough away, that he had finished his trip and returned.

Jesus, there was no way to judge if it would be safe to leave. That tiger asshole Ted was stretched out at the back of the hut, sitting there, smug, like he had swatted a fly. He was back in that same spot he held me hostage from for weeks now, basking in the sun.

I stood there panting, while white rage rose in me. My eyes widened and with every fibre of my being I screamed *'Fuck this, fuck you Ted.'*

Then without warning and what I describe as divine intervention, I kicked the door open. I stuck the curtain pole into Ted's chest and then his throat. He was on his back and I was standing behind his head. He could not reach me with his swipes.

Images rapidly flashed before my eyes. First, it was Shane with his beautiful face. He was younger with dreadlocks. Tears drenched his face after another emotional battering. I held on tight.

Ted was not able to release himself from the pole. He tried to swipe me again as I twisted the pole. Then I saw Mam, her big brown eyes bulging as she was choked against the kitchen wall. Her sweet red apron all bunched up in between their bodies.

Ted was roaring and writhing on the porch beneath me with force beyond belief. I did not relent. Next, I saw myself a nine-year-old girl, pale and frozen in fear.

It was then that an almighty power and strength came over me. I repeatedly stabbed him in the throat. As he roared, I slammed the pole down his throat and out the back of his neck. I pushed past his spine and nailed the pole through him and into the wooden decking back porch. Blood sprayed from his neck and splattered all over my own neck and face. I barely noticed.

I stood over him for a moment and then caught my reflection in what was left of the back door window. I was unrecognisable to myself. I stood there, staring. After a minute of being in a haze I became clear about what I had to do next.

I had to run, fast and far. I did not know if he would somehow get back up.

Adrenaline soared through my body and I ran away backwards to see if he was getting up or coming after me. It was then I realised he was not moving at all. He was not injured. He was dead. I managed to kill Ted.

I was the calmest I had been in weeks. I felt strong and powerful. I did not stop running. I slowed down for a minute and momentarily I felt a bit of grief and guilt.

Despite him keeping me hostage and hurting me, I had not wanted him dead. I needed to be free of him. I had to live and so did my beautiful baby.

Dying was not an option. Living as a hostage while going crazy, that was not an option either. No one was going to save me. I had to save myself. It was me or him. I had to choose me.

12

*T*hings seemed to be happening fast at the airport. People were talking loudly and moving quickly. I was used to silence except for the sound of Ted and birds.

Before I knew it, I was ushered by the desk staff onto the plane. It seemed life went on in the real world while I was hauled up in a hut.

Once I collapsed into my comfy aisle seat I turned to Charlie. Tears and love flowed between us. Poor Charlie. He looked like a wreck not knowing where I was gone to emotionally during that time.

The last he saw of me as my former self I had been running away into a sand dune to pee. Then I had been taken over by emotional pain and entered a strange state.

That morning before we got the flight, I gagged at everything from morning sickness. The all-you-can-eat breakfast at the hotel was full of reams of cold meats and hot eggs. It had been an obstacle course to be mastered.

I collected toast and a croissant. The baby was insisting carbohydrates alone be consumed. I found a seat outside at the edge of the large hotel decking farthest away from everyone.

Except of course for Charlie and his morning eggs. I laughed while I told him that 'our first real challenge as husband and wife is for you to keep that eggy whiff away from me.'

He did his best. We both knew the real task was for me to

hold on to my sanity while the painful truth of my past revisited me.

We discussed what we would call the baby. If it was to be a girl, we wanted to call her Joy. The plane shook, then dropped quickly and shook again. I heard passengers all around me raising their voices in concern.

The woman beside me was frantically clutching at the armrest between us saying, 'Oh, Jesus, Mary and Joseph. Oh, God help us.' She grabbed my arm. I did not flinch. I was immune to what I perceived as the fake danger we were in. I was not going to be breaking a sweat unless the plane actually starting to go down.

My initial sense of relief that the tiger torment was over was leaving me and my mood began to deteriorate. The glory I experienced after escaping Ted was fleeting. It was quickly replaced by feelings akin to grief. Those old familiar feelings filled me with dread.

My tolerance was low. I muttered under my breath, 'Cop on, woman, Cop. The. Fuck. On.'

She must have heard me. 'Sorry, did you say something to me?'

I pretended not to hear her; I was now in full on cranky form.

Grief makes trivial things even less important. Yet parallel to that it was the small things bothering me. My brain found this hard to reconcile. My eyes were heavy.

While held hostage, inside that hut I often felt confused. If I fell asleep, it was hard to tell if it was day or night when I woke up. A quiet desperation inside helped me through. I visualized going home. I pictured Charlie with me on the plane and our life ahead if us.

The reality was not matching the vision. I believed I would feel elated and excited about my reunion with my loved ones. Instead, I felt fearful, drained, and empty. It was over and it did not feel that way.

Grieving for Ted and my former self was confusing to me. The experience changed me. I used to laugh a lot. That is how I noticed I was grieving for my former frivolous self: the Lucy who laughed a lot.

When I got off the plane Brona and Hilary awaited me with open arms and smiles. They wanted to surprise us with a fridge full of food and a lovely lunch. I felt numb. I wished to God that Ted had not put me in that position, where it had to be him or me.

With Charlie beside me in his familiar blue jeans dragging along the ground, his unruly hair and his black V-neck jumper I felt better. His hugs were so tight I could barely breathe. I was never leaving his side again.

I longed for it to have been different and that Charlie and I had a normal honeymoon. Yet I managed to smile again because I was with him.

I still felt my boots were stained with blood from my leg where Ted had sliced it open. I felt I had ingested his blood as it sprayed into my mouth and I was contaminated.

At home I embraced everything fresh with a deep desperation. I relished the warm plentiful water on my skin until it ran out. I wrapped the crisp sheets tight around me. Being cold was an old familiar feeling I now found comforting.

I tried to absorb my senses into each moment and to be present. This helped. Some nights I slept soundly. Others, I tossed and turned, dreaming I was alone again in the dark, unable to see anything but able to feel Ted's hairy face and his horrid breath on me.

Occasionally it went up a level from a nightmare to a night terror. One night I dreamt Ted pinned me to the floor. No matter what I did I could not escape him. The dream was so scary and life-like that when I woke up I felt I was still in the dream. I was too terrified to move.

Charlie, a warm snoring mound in the bed beside me was fast asleep, breathing deeply and calmly. All I had to do was lift my arm to touch him or to call out his name, but I was too paralysed with fear.

I was drenched in sweat too. This meant I had to get out of bed once I got myself together and change my pyjamas. I was always amazed how damp they were. It was scary how much sweating and turmoil I must have gone through before I finally woke myself from the night terrors.

Constantly living with a level of fear is exhausting. The night terrors left me depleted physically and emotionally. I did not know who to turn to or how to explain the ordeal to anyone. It was another thing along with my disease of alcoholism I was ashamed of.

I did not want to let it impact on Charlie and me as newlyweds. I escaped Ted and I was home, but I felt trapped. I turned to prayer for acceptance of what had happened and to feel good again.

I returned to my mindfulness and meditation. I believed if I stayed in the moment, I would be ok. I began to notice nature again: small flowers on the roadside. A ladybird on a leaf. I promised myself if I got my joy in life back I would never take it for granted again.

I survived other ordeals and managed to regain energy and contentment. I wanted to feel that way again. In an attempt to remind myself of who I was, I intentionally jogged some happy memories of myself as a child. I was innocent and harmless back then.

One of my earliest memories is being woken in my cot to a squished and ridiculously cute doll face with huge chocolate brown eyes peering at me between the bars. I was delighted by my little brother Dan.

It surprised me to hear from my parents that apparently one morning as I walked by, I squished the back of his neck with my little bare foot. Mam told Dad I was a little bit jealous of Dan.

When she was changing his nappy, I bit her on the elbow and left an imprint with my six milk teeth. Paula had her own turn at being green-eyed too. When I was brought home to meet the family, she did not know what to make of me and so she ignored me for the first while.

Mam dressed Paula and me in matching outfits regularly but there was no way to make us look related. We just had the big blue eyes in common.

Growing up, Paula teased me for being the shortest in the family and said that I must be adopted. I did look different from my siblings. They all had brown hair and mine was strawberry blonde. From a young age I concluded I was adopted. Shane and Kerry reassured me I was not. They looked out for us three younger ones.

The five of us muddled along well together, oblivious to the fact we were actually minding each other. Shane and Kerry went off on their own adventures, but never for too long.

Some nights when Mam and Dad thought we were asleep, we crawled downstairs and around the house, playing our invented game called 'sneaking around the house.' We rarely seemed to get caught.

Dad was fast asleep from early in the evening to prepare for his early morning shift at the factory. If we made too much noise, he banged his bedroom floor with a big metal rod. That noise shook through to the sitting room ceiling as a warning for us children and Mam to be quiet so he could go back asleep.

Mam often stayed up late and was a self-confessed night owl, watching television until she fell asleep on the chair. Her false teeth rattled while she snored and woke her up. She toddled off to bed and slept on late in the mornings while we got ourselves ready for school.

When she was pregnant with me, she fell and broke all her top teeth. The dentist took them all out. That is how she ended up with the false ones. That cannot have made Dad take to me much either. That and the fact I was a girl.

From a young age I realised it was that he was disinterested in me more than disliked me and that became the norm.

Aunty Clare told me once at a family get together in a pub that she had looked after me for the first few months of my life because Mam was not well. Afterwards I asked Dad how often he was able to see me. Without even glancing at me he said, 'I didn't.'

'But why not?' I tried to conceal the hurt in my voice.

He looked at me, while rolling his eyes 'Sure I didn't even have a car.'

Surely, he had a bicycle or there was a bus route to take to see me. I did not dare voice those obvious options. Instead, I asked. 'Not even once?'

He did not answer me, so I left it there.

It was not worth the anger it might evoke or him telling me to 'get a grip and stop being so bloody sensitive.' I was already too hurt to hear that tripe.

When I came along, they had two daughters already and all the pregnancies up until then had been planned. He was probably hoping I was at least going to be a second son. But no, alas, I was another girl and because I had a voice and I used it I was deemed as a cheeky tomboy. His worst nightmare.

Mam said I tried to relay what was an adventure to me as a five-year-old and he found it 'a bit irritating.' I was to be seen and not heard and certainly not full of opinions and ideas. I was to 'get off the stage' and 'shush.'

I liked that he worked the evening shifts, and it was Mam and us in the house. Dad liked to micromanage us. Mam assumed we were behaving ourselves and the atmosphere was completely different

Brona was often in my house and always more glamorous than me, her mam liked to dress her in silk blouses, long skirts, and fancy belts. I was quite happy in my rolled-up jeans and t-shirts or white shirts with flowers on them.

Mam had more clothes in her wardrobe and bedroom than all the rest of us put together. When she was suffering from mania, she bought loads of stuff. Back then door to door sales or phone orders from catalogues were the only way to shop from home. Dad tried to use us as spies to tell him if she was getting deliveries. I never told him.

I felt sorry for Mam. *So what if she wanted a gazillion*

blouses and Tupperware boxes. Her life with him was shite. She deserved them.

His idea of doing something nice for her was drowning rats in the back garden. Mam was utterly terrified of rats. Our neighbour had taken to storing her rubbish between her garage and our hedges in the back garden. This created a big rat problem. They were everywhere and even came up and managed to climb on the wall outside the back door.

Instead of calling pest control and putting down poison Dad brought home a large grey bin on wheels. They used them in the factory for collecting up spare materials.

He used it to plunge the rats he caught in a box trap into cold water. One of the walls of the box trap was mesh and as each drowning rat squealed it also gripped the mesh with its yellow teeth in an attempt to save itself.

Dad used a metal rod to push the box back under the water. As I was not that much taller than the bath, witnessing this felt as if I was almost face to face with the squealing rat. My skin crawls to this day remembering that. What a barbaric thing for him to do and to let us watch.

He had little regard for animals. When Shane was a teenager, he had a terrapin he loved dearly for years. One morning I found him sobbing in his bedroom, holding the tiny turtle. Dad had unplugged the water heater in the tank during the night. He said he found it too noisy. Dad laughed it off, but Shane was heartbroken. His pet was dead.

Shane soon got rabbits. When Dad got sick of them, in a fit of anger, he put them in a cardboard box. With Shane in his car, he drove around until he found two guys on the street to take them. I saw Shane cry that day too.

The next grand gesture from Dad for Mam was a red phone he bought for her. She was so happy that we got a landline phone. She rang in some of her orders for makeup and cosmetics. She also phoned her friends in the ladies' club and my aunties.

Her best friend in the ladies' club lived in our cul-de-sac. She turned up at our front door every Wednesday night wearing a blue head scarf wrapped around her face and with her pink lipstick all over her teeth. Mam used to leave her waiting in the porch. She never brought her in or mentioned to her she had lipstick on her teeth.

If Mam decided she did not want to go the ladies club, she made me or Paula phone her friend with some elaborate excuse she got us to invent. She did not know how to be assertive in even the most basic of ways.

Previously we used the village phone box or people called Mam on the other neighbour's phone. At least now we actually had a phone. I think Dad regretted getting it.

Mam used to ring him at work and shout down the phone that he was a pervert and that he was flirting with the factory girls. They had shouting matches and he made out she was paranoid. I think it drove her a bit mad. I do not think she had any idea he was gas lighting her.

Being eleven and twelve years old, Brona and I needed to phone often to discuss firstly outfits and secondly which boy was chasing which girl now. From a young age I wanted to be like Kerry and her friends; they wore denim jackets and high heels to the discos. At the weekends I watched Kerry from my bunkbed getting all dolled up, putting on pink lipstick and fruity perfume.

I pleaded with her to take me to town. I wanted to get a denim jacket and lipstick too. I could not wait until it was my turn to have drinks and go dancing.

During the summer we did not see our friends because every year for the whole summer Dad borrowed an old house in Longford from his friend for us. He came down for the first and the last week, otherwise he was back in Dublin working. It was the highlight of my childhood.

Each year my parents packed us five children, clothes, food, toys, and books into and on top of our old green station wagon. The first year we went Paula and I counted down the one hundred and nineteen kilometres as we drove.

It took nearly all day to get there. We were slowed down by many bathroom breaks, food stops and emergency pulling in for turn taking to vomit at the side of the road.

I was squashed in between Paula and Kerry on one side and Shane and Dan on the other. The first year we arrived late in the evening. It was dark and on the narrow winding lane to the holiday home we were greeted by a local farmer's barking dog.

Dad did not see him coming and did not slow down. He accidently hit him with the car. He jumped out frantically but the dog quickly scampered off appearing unhurt. That woke us all up in time to arrive at the house.

It was a small house but the three acres it sat on was the biggest field we had ever seen in our lives. The sound of crickets in this enormous field confirmed we were somewhere exotic and fascinating.

Inside there were two bedrooms upstairs that were useable. There was a third abandoned bedroom downstairs. It was freezing cold and had a huge Michael Jackson 'Thriller' poster above a very dusty old pink mattress. We concluded among ourselves that someone must have died in there.

We decided we were going to ignore the 'scary room.' Forever. I never liked to be alone anywhere downstairs in that house.

Upstairs, our bedroom was large and bright, with exposed mahogany wooden floors and a ceiling window. I had never seen a slanted roof with a window in it.

We all piled into bed. Shane and Dan were in a huge wrought iron single bed on one side of the room. It looked like it had been there for one hundred years. Kerry, Paula and I were zipped up together into two sleeping bags in the equally antiquated double bed on the other side of the room.

Despite the mattress being mashed to the same depth and sponginess as a slice of bread we fell asleep on the springs to the sound of crickets chirping.

During the night I woke to the sound of the front door opening and closing and someone going outside. I crept out of my shared sleeping bag, creaked across the old wooden floor and looked out the window down to the moonlit field. My eyes adjusted and I saw Dad there among the long grass with his back to the house.

He was in his navy pyjama bottoms and a white vest. He was holding the sweeping brush high above his head. He appeared to be intensely watching something in the grass. Suddenly, he smashed the brush into the long grass repeatedly. It seemed he had enough; he was putting an end to the choir of crickets.

13

In the morning, Dan, Paula, Shane and I went outside to the magical mystery surrounds to explore. We looked for the crickets we heard the night before. We made our way running through fields and hedges until I no longer knew where our field was. I knew Shane would get us back.

We ran through the overgrown grass and stopped in front of a derelict house. Looking at each other, without uttering a word, we knew we were going in to investigate. Shane went in first. The front door creaked open easily.

He slowly led the way across some broken floorboards. Inside was tiny. There were two rooms. It looked like someone left in a hurry years before. There was a bedroom with a double bed and a nightdress left behind on the bed. There were all kinds of old essentials around the place and a pillow on the floor. It had an old bloodstain on it. That shook us up a bit.

The kitchen and living area were combined, with sparse furniture and all the crockery was thickly covered in dust. Someone had decided to store hay bales on one side of the room. Shane picked up a teapot and inspected it.

He found a letter and read out that it was addressed to a Mr. and Mrs. Sombre. We decided even their name was spooky and we left. Shane took the teapot with him and placed a piece of hay between the door handle and the frame. He wanted to know if anyone else was coming in or out.

We ran away full of nervous excitement and eventually

ended up at the edge of the narrow part of the River Inny. There was a small blue wood rowing boat floating a foot away. Shane pulled it to the edge of the lake. Paula, Dan, and I climbed in.

He waded into the waters filled with mud and reeds and announced that it was not very deep and dragged us in the boat across the lake. Over halfway across he lost his footing and clung to the boat to stop himself from going under. I stopped breathing until he was wading along again.

At the other side of the lake we found a cottage with a weathered sign saying 'Mini Jo's shop.' Inside we discovered it was a shelf in his house rather than a shop. Jo sold sweets and that was all that mattered to us.

On our way we found mushrooms growing in a hilly field which Mam added to the dinner. She was likely thinking that was our biggest discovery of the day. We did not mention the old cottage exploration or the boat trip to the shop.

The days rolled into weeks. Dad was back for the final week. We played Tetris with all our belongings to try to squish everything back into the car for the return to Dublin.

We entered our cul-de-sac to the cheers of our friends. Soon I was back out on the green playing Rounders with my friends and at school swapping stories with Brona. I spent my classes daydreaming about our summer in Longford. I wished I was back there living in that bubble of freedom forever.

It became clearer to me how I could try to recover from the trauma of being held hostage from my beautiful life. I had to turn back to nature yet again. Even as a child I was at my happiest in nature. Forest walks with Shane and being in the park with Brona and Dan.

The seafront had been my sanctuary over the years. Being there healed me through the aftermath of Shane's death and through the first two difficult years in recovery. It had been my higher power.

I spent a lot of time in nature over the coming months. I made sure I looked after myself and the baby as much as possible. I was planning a peaceful water birth, but I knew it would be bound to have its moments. I tried to keep as fit and healthy as possible during the pregnancy.

Daily I took my baby bump over the local grey brick bridge with the dandelions growing out of the wall. I told my baby we used to call them 'wet the beds' as children. This is what I had been told: if you picked them, you would wet the bed.

As we walked down the dirt hill pebbled with gravel to the canal side, I heard two young boys shout excitedly to their friend that they had found a hurl. They were plucking stones from the side of the canal bank and trying to hit them with the hurl over to the train track that runs parallel to the canal.

A hammering noise on the other side of them from behind all the brambles drew my attention. I looked into a sports club field. I saw a funeral home I had never noticed it before. I was reminded of the occasion I last saw Shane.

I told my baby all about their beautiful uncle up in heaven. That he loved nature so much that he would have loved to be on the walk with us. I explained that he would always be watching over us and whenever we needed help, he will walk beside us.

A gentle cool breeze on my face and hands brought me back to where I was. I took in the calming water of the canal. There was not one cloud in the sky on this sunny mid-April day. A duck leapt out of the canal and circled above us, celebratory of the freedom of the beautiful weather and that there were no other people or even ducks nearby. It was almost playful.

My eye was drawn through the hedges and brambles again. I looked past the thick holly and thorny bushes. Seeds had been sown in a large field. It was starting to peek through the earth. Tiny green shoots springing to life.

Even the noise of the commuter train combined with a plane flying by did not disturb the sense of peace and beauty. I spotted a white feather on the ground. I told my baby how some of my friends have come to believe that finding one means an angel is with you. In that moment I felt blessed as if we had angels with us.

Through the heat haze up ahead I saw some boats. As I reached the boats a bird suddenly flew from a tree and lost a white feather. It floated down alongside us and landed beside my foot. I felt the angels confirming they were with us, or Shane was having fun saying hi. It made my heart swell and I smiled too.

I wanted to pick it up but at that same moment a cyclist saluted me as he went by and I left it there. I took a rest on a shiny black bench; it had been placed right beside a smaller very old and basic wooden bench. I wondered who sat there before me and who would sit where we were afterwards.

We turned back for home. As we neared the bridge, I was jolted from my nature bubble by the noise of a match that was now going on. Six-year-olds were being cheered on at tag rugby practice by their proud parents. It reminded me of Dan playing from such an early age.

I told the baby I was very proud to get to be their mammy. With the birds singing in my ears, the sunshine on my face and the tiniest white butterfly approaching us I explained how lucky I felt to have such a beautiful place to walk.

As the months went on my massive baby bump slowed my walking down. I chomped my way through the rest of that pregnancy, addicted to pineapple, mandarins and Tangle Twister ice pops.

Most nights I took a bowl of mandarins to bed. Charlie regularly awoke in the early hours of the morning to me munching through them, barely taking a breath. When the cravings came the baby had to have them all, immediately, and did a jig on my ribs from the natural sugar high.

Joy was over one year old when Shane's anniversary came around again. I was surprised at how quickly I sank pretty low about his death again. How he died was something I could not reconcile.

It hit me hard how sad it was that he was not here to meet Joy and for her to meet him. I wished they would have experienced each other's company and shared their wonderfulness together.

He would have been an amazing uncle to her. I cried many tears. I knew I had to do something. I had to move past this grief for Shane. He would want me to.

Even though I travelled to Thailand and put a lotus in a tabernacle. I wrote Shane a twenty-six page later and I cried a lot. Years had gone by and I was still not okay with his absence.

Yes, I now felt I had a closer bond with him. We chatted and I felt he had my back. Yet each November the trauma of how he died hit me again. No matter how hard I tried to bunker down and let the grief storm pass. No matter how much gratitude and positivity and love I had in my life I could not help but get traumatised again. His parting from us in the manner that he chose devastated me every year.

I was trapped inside that Don McLean sad song for the week of his anniversary each year. The lyrics reducing me to tears, *Starry Starry night. Weathered faces lined in pain. Now I understand what you tried to say to me and how you suffered for your sanity. You took your life as lovers often do.*

Things had to change. I did not want a weathered face lined in pain. It was not going to be good for me or good enough for my baby if I was crying and feeling low every November. It was my turn to be my happiest. I wanted laughter lines around my eyes and to have character within my eyes from years of making the most of everything.

My first sponsor returned to America. Her sponsor Marie a wonderfully wise older woman was my new sponsor. She told me it was up to me to ensure for myself and my family that I moved past the trauma of how he died. We deserved it and so did he.

I wanted to focus solely on the good life he lived and all the things he taught me. Charlie was patient, telling me,

'It's okay, Lucy. You cannot help how you feel.'

I wanted to change how I felt about it. So, I returned to Shane's grave for first time since before I got married. Ten years had passed since Shane died. The patch of earth where his remains resided never provided much comfort for me, so I did not go often.

Yet, I could not stand the tragic memory of that November day any longer. I needed a new one. It seemed bonkers, even to me, but I decided I would create a new happy November memory with Shane, even though he was dead.

Since I escaped and survived my entrapment from Ted I was determined to let go of any sadness from my past. I promised myself, yet again, if I got happy again, I would never let anything bring me down for too long. I had to keep that promise for myself and my beautiful family. I had to fight my emotional battles and dispel my demons of the past.

I brought a picnic with me, a ham sandwich, Emerald sweets, Shane's favourite and cheese Doritos, a nod to our last snack together. I got a cup of tea from the garage, parked outside the graveyard, and in I trotted to his grave.

I felt half cracked and more grounded about his death than ever before as I snacked on his graveside. I sat on the edge looking at his headstone and his photo on the corner. It is the same as the one I have at home, his face smiling in a woolly jumper. His long hair tied back, legs casually crossed. Even then I asked myself, *is it real that he is gone?* The answer was simply, *yes*.

Initially I was force feeding the picnic down. I wished I was having a cider and a smoke with him instead. But I was not, and I would not. My life was too good to mess it up.

I got up from his graveside and sat on the chilly stone surround of the grave directly across from him. I wanted to take in the full view of his grave.

I looked around the graveyard thinking, *I drove for two hours all the way from the countryside to Dublin. I've had the picnic, what now?*

I sat there a while longer and something changed. Shane and I had a conversation. I told him 'I miss you, big brother. You have a beautiful new niece called Joy, but I bet you know this already. I bet you were there when I put that lotus in the tabernacle.'

I paused as if he was going to answer. 'I'm sorry I have not talked to you more. I couldn't feel you around. I have such a lovely life with Charlie. All the family stuff drags me down. If you have a solution, let me know. I just want it to be easy, you know? I know you get that, Shane.'

I listened carefully and I knew he was listening to me. I felt it. It dawned on me, *he is not on the earth in a physical sense anymore and I am, but we can share it.*

A fact I learned in science class long ago popped into my head. *Energy cannot be destroyed it can only be transferred.* Shane was not destroyed, nor was his energy, it was transferred.

Who would have thought after all my spiritual searching it was a scientific fact that helped me get closure on how Shane died. It showed me his spirit is here.

All the years I spent bemoaning my beloved brother seemed futile now. The notion of the amount of pain I was enduring was a testament to how much I loved him. Yes, this was true on one level.

Here I was, the one promoting that everyone who knew Shane should try to remember how he lived and not how he died. Yet I spent the last number of years so stuck on the fact that he was gone in the physical sense.

I was missing two majorly important points. The first was that when I was focusing on him being gone in body it was not possible for me to focus on his energy that was still around or to connect to it. I finally did that day, properly and I have continued to do so since then.

Ironically, when I finally tried to let him go fully was when I got him back. Maybe even telling myself in Thailand he was gone physically but I could still communicate with him helped me. All this paved the way for me to get to this understanding.

The second important point I was missing out on when I was focusing on Shane being gone from my life as a living being was this: when I was thinking or feeling sad about the life, he was not living with me, I was not being grateful enough for the life we had together.

Shane was on this earth for thirty-two years. He spent a fair amount of that time with me. I learned so much from him. He taught me about life, unconditional love and the importance of being authentic.

Every day I can express gratitude for all the gold we had together in this life. Our nature trails, his love of music and books and people; all loves I shared too and continue to do so. The laughs we had, the tea, the wine, the parties, the tears. Shane and I had a big brother and little sister bond that was ours and is still ours.

Tears flow as I write these words. I imagine he is here beside me perhaps behind me saying *don't cry, little sis*. A cow in the field outside is mooing loudly, making me laugh.

Today I do not have to cry a river when I miss him in the physical form. I just remind myself his spirit is around. Finally, by his graveside I found a way to accept what I thought was the unacceptable. Nothing stirred around me in the graveyard except for my heart lifting.

I was ready to go home to my beautiful life with Charlie and Joy. As I was driving home Bob Marley's song *Three Little Birds* came on the radio. The song that always gave me a lump in my throat, not this time. I cannot help thinking it was him and did not make me sad.

I know I cannot make the big Shane-shaped influence on my heart, my soul or my life any smaller. I cannot shrink my grief. I can focus and lavish love and attention on all the good memories of him and on the good people in my life. Finally, after years I have grown bigger than the grief.

The next morning, I filled Charlie in on my experience. As always, he took all my tales in his stride. The news of a picnic at Shane graveside did not seem to ruffle him at all.

I was unusually tired, but I put it down to the driving and emotion of the trip to the graveyard. That was until Charlie served us up our breakfast eggs and an old familiar feeling of nausea overwhelmed me. I pushed the plate away, muttering, 'Oh, God, the smell.'

Charlie and I locked eyes over Joy's head. I knew we were both thinking the same thing. *Could this mean what we think it means? Have we been so lucky as to get pregnant so easily again?*

We were indeed blessed again, and we welcomed our wonderful daughter Hope into the world. Becoming a mammy is without a doubt the biggest turning point in my life. It created the biggest, strongest, best and most definite line in the sand for me to never step back over.

I promised myself I will never allow my children to go through the same as I did. They will always come first. There were many important lines before. Like how life was before and then after the death of Shane.

The lines of how my life was before and after going back to college and realising I could learn. Life before and after I tackled my addiction. Finally, life before I escaped from Ted.

Before Charlie and I got married I turned to my Earthsong friend Adam for advice. I phoned him concerned. 'I'm worried I will ruin Charlie's life, what if I start drinking again? Or what if he ruins my life?'

'Lucy, you are both stepping into the ring of fire and it will transform you.'

I think I understand that now. The best thing he told me was that himself and his wife 'neither judge nor indulge each other.'

I shared this with Charlie, and we agreed that is a great way to try to be. It is much easier said than done and we are work in progress. We are happy and imperfect and that is ok for us.

When I had my children, and I became a member of a loving family. I went from bobbing around at sea alone without real direction or purpose, to being ashore with them.

The gift of pure unconditional love for my children and the bounty of love that comes from being a mammy has made me the happiest I can ever be. That is a shore I never ever wish to leave. They have made my life worth living. Every, single, day.

I will never understand where Mam was when her cubs needed her to roar for them. My girls are much too distract-ing and delicious to focus on anything negative for too long.

Hope has a pixie face framed by fair curls with big playful green eyes. She is an old soul and has been here before. It is hard to find words for such a sight. It is uncanny how alike Shane she is in her looks and her energy.

I wondered was I seeing something that was not there but Brona and Hilary both tell me regularly how similar she looks to her Uncle Shane.

Both Joy and Hope are equally and utterly loveable from the tops of their tiny locks to the tips of their teeny painted toenails. I cannot imagine my life without them. They are my biggest blessings, and they always will be.

My children are like two different sides of the same star. Completely different perspectives yet both shine equally as bright. Lighting up with life everywhere they go by being themselves. I pray they stay that way. I will always encourage them to be themselves strongly and happily.

14

It is much easier for me to stand up for my children than myself. My roar is always on standby for them. If you are a bigger child being rough in a baby's play area you are going to hear my roar. If you think it is okay to kiss my child on the lips when you have a cold sore or not, you are most definitely going to hear my roar.

It is spontaneous and instant when it comes to them. They cannot defend themselves yet, so I will. When it comes to me, well, it took a lot longer for me to find my voice. You see, after years of turmoil I finally went to the police and reported the man who abused me as a child. Ted.

He was someone who should have loved and protected me. He did the opposite. He abused me.

Revealing this to my family and subsequently the police took overcoming as much fear and mustering up as much courage and strength as it would to kill that tiger with my bare hands. Maybe even more.

I was abused by Ted and when I confronted him, he denied it.

I told my family. Most of them denied it too.

He turned Mam and nearly all my siblings against me, causing me so much pain and isolation.

I got stuck in a rut of fear. Pain and isolation subsumed me. I was unsure if or how I could get out of it and back to my life. I felt trapped by Ted's actions and subsequent lies and I was imprisoned in pain.

Even though I did escape the pain it was hard to enjoy all

I had because I was so hurt. I needed so much time to heal. To escape Ted for good I had to lose nearly all of my family of origin.

I was at the point where I could no longer deny the image, I had of Ted abusing me as the truth. Or live with the fear of him striking again with my nieces or nephews. I desperately wanted it to be a dream, a memory gone wrong, a bad scene in a movie.

I had been nine years of age and I have no memory of life before then. My first memory is in fact from a photograph I saw. For years I pretended to myself and others that I remembered being in the cot, but I do not.

I have nightmares of me being in the cot at age two but no actual memory. My love of photos stems from the fact that they tell me about my childhood. I get to see what I did and how I looked.

No matter how hard I try I cannot remember. Mam cannot remember much either. She told me in the past that the electroconvulsive treatment wiped out memories of certain times in her life.

No matter how much I tried to forget or no matter how many years I pickled my brain in cider for that memory did not wash away.

I was finally sober for long enough and strong enough to admit to myself why I was always uncomfortable around Ted. Why I cringed when he would make embarrassing comments in relation to my appearance or clothes.

I was alarmed and intensely uncomfortable. I hated him leaning over me when he was in our tiny kitchen. I hated being so close with his bad breath and body odour.

Once I admitted out loud what he was like, memories came back to me. I remember being in bed one night and he came in after a parent-teacher meeting. He kneeled down and made me smell his breath for Guinness. He was uncomfortably close to my face, breathing on me.

It made me nauseous. I was trying not to smell anything by holding my own breath, but of course I told him 'no' so he would back off me. There was no way I was going to risk him flying into a rage.

Once Shane died, he mellowed and worked hard on his Mr Nice Guy routine. Mam was constantly heavily medicated since then.

Perhaps that is how she coped. She sat in the same spot in their sitting room, sitting and staring day after day. No one could tell if it was by choice or from too much medication for too long. This was to the point where she was dependent on others to zip up her coat.

It was sad to see how Mam was ending up. We would come by to visit, one by one. Like beings from another planet revolving around this mostly silent being. She appeared stationary and calm but for many years it was as if there was a storm raging behind the silence. Eventually she resembled a shipwrecked vessel sitting on the sofa, surely with so many stories to tell.

I wished so much she would talk to me. For years I was desperate for her to see me and to know me and to let me know her. To her we were perhaps a fast-forwarding movie in a foreign language with no subtitles. I was always trying to translate.

I used to hear myself, my voice trying too hard to tell her how I felt. Undertones of pleas, 'Do you know I'm trying to reach you? You know you are the only mother that I have? I love you. I wish I could have you in my world along with me, for you to let me back into yours.'

She was silent.

'I long for you to share your dreams and for you to experience some joy at my babies and their milestones. You're here but you are gone. The loss of Shane so soon, well, there are no words for your sadness. Is that why there are no words at all? The struggle you're lost in stifles you from living. You shuffle along, trying to keep up.'

Silence.

'I try not to cause you pain; therefore, I don't do much about it anymore. Except to tell you that I love you and its okay to be you.'

Again, Mam was silent.

Still the question harbours in my mind and heart: *can we not somehow bring back Mam? She has been replaced by this woman that sits and stares with no confidence and eventually no competence. No control.*

As a tween and teenager I spent years as her unpaid therapist. Every night I listened to her tales of grief and woe about her own father's sudden death by heart attack while she was pregnant with Shane.

The guilt was immense.

I would get all dolled up to go out with my friends on a Saturday night. Mam would let me know how lonely she was going to be. I was a ball of anxiety and upset so I would drink too much.

The alcohol helped me put on a happy face and eventually by the end of the night my mask would slip from all the tears bubbling out from under it.

I tried to trust boyfriends. I attracted some sweet guys, but I always went for the boys who eventually hurt me.

Over the years it was as if Ted was jealous of our boy-friends. This made me hugely uncomfortable, yet he always tried to make Mam look like the jealous crazy one.

He continued to gaslight her and make out she was crazy.

I should have known what to expect when I eventually told the truth. I was not prepared for the onslaught.

I started with Paula; we had been the closet for the longest over the years. She had been off with me since her last visit.

Charlie, Joy, and I were staying down the road in Kerry's house, while she was abroad. We were minding the house while we were waiting for a new house, we were moving county to the countryside.

Paula and Mam did not come down to us. I asked them to come to see us, instead, there was a silent protest. They walked by the house we were staying in to go to the local park without us. I was beyond hurt. I think they must have been trying to make a point because I was avoiding Ted.

Paula returned to America and sent me an email from there saying she was cutting me off. I always forgave her, bending over backwards for our relationship to survive.

Again, I was trying to fix things so I figured telling her why I was avoiding Ted's company might help. I phoned her and told her the reason I did not go up to his house while she was home was because I was not comfortable being in his company.

I told her 'He abused me as a child.'

She said she believed me. Paula said she had her own concerns about him and his bizarre behaviour. She reminded me how he had been shaming towards me on a family holiday when her husband was with us.

He sent Mam into the bedroom after me when I got out of the shower to tell me 'Ted says you are to get dressed before he gets back.'

He being my sister's husband, as if I was going to prance around naked like some crazy woman. I cried in the room, wondering what I had done to be treated as a temptress. All I did was shower and discreetly cross a hall out of sight of anyone, to go into a room and get ready.

He tormented me on the holiday saying I was swimming after men in the sea. Despite not being a strong swimmer, I was actually trying to go further out to sea to get away from him and his leer.

It was clear now after I spoke to Paula that I was not the only one who knew his thinking was fucked. I thanked her for the chat. I was relieved someone else knew what he was like. She never mentioned it again until months later.

By then I plucked up enough courage to tell Dan too. I met him on neutral territory in a café. Which, in hindsight, was wrong on my part. I had no experience of how to tell my brother that Ted abused me.

He was visibly upset. We went for a walk near the café, and he was crossing roads and walking in and out of the car park. We sat in his car, but he was so distressed it was hard to talk. I tried to support him. It was so hard to see him that upset.

I did not like having to tell him, but he now had small children too. He needed to know. The conversation was about how upset he was rather than how it impacted me. He said he wanted to believe me, not that he did believe me and asked could he confront Ted. I agreed. I was not going to disappear under a rock.

The next day Dan phoned me, he wanted to know exactly what happened. I refused to tell him. I was horrified and mortified at being asked. It felt like I needed to provide evidence. I said I did not want to go there. I could not.

He called again a few days later after he spoke to Ted. It was clear he did a good number on poor Dan's head, putting on the waterworks and pleading innocent. It killed me to see Dan hurting so much and desperately not wanting it to be true. I wished it was not my reality either.

Dan had no proof and Ted was lying his face off. His tone was different. It was obvious he had gone from wanting to believe me to being on the fence. He did not know who to believe. Dan wanted me to tell Kerry immediately with her having children, in fact, he demanded it.

I had every intention of telling her next. First, I needed a day to reduce my stress levels for the sake of my unborn baby. I was heavily pregnant with Hope at this point, and I was so worried the impact all of this might be having on her too.

One of the main reasons I told the family was to protect my nieces and nephews. I had to protect my own children too. I braced myself for telling Kerry. Even though she had been good to me at times in the past, she was cold when she wanted to be.

Things were already strained between us since my engagement and wedding. I knew if she was not getting her own way, she could turn on me. I knew this revelation might cause havoc but I love my nieces and nephews almost as if they are my own, so I had to tell her, for them.

I asked Kerry to meet me at a mediated session with a therapist as by now I was eight months pregnant. I could not face her going nuts and shouting at me or having to deal with her alone. I also thought that she would probably be upset and would need support.

We sat in the therapist's sitting room on big comfortable white couches. For me this was starkly contrasted by feeling almost the most uncomfortable internally as I ever had as an adult.

Kerry sat on one side with the therapist, and I sat on the other. It was hot, coupled with my massive pregnancy bump and the stress I was in a sweat.

The mediator said to Kerry, 'Lucy invited you here today, Kerry, because she wants to share some difficult information with you.'

Kerry sat there on the edge of her seat with a blank expression staring at me. 'I want you to know why I don't want to be in Ted's company. It's because he was inappropriate with me as a child.'

Her expression changed immediately to one of determination. It appeared that she had decided how she was going to handle this. Kerry did not respond to me. Instead, she looked at the therapist and said, 'I have a very different relationship with Ted. I am going to have to detach.'

My heart sank. I asked, 'Detach, from who, Kerry?'

She said, again to the therapist, 'My kids will want Ted at our family occasions.'

She glanced at me. 'So would it be best to not tell you when I'm having one?'

Huh? What the hell? She couldn't be serious? Oh, she was.

Kerry instantly decided one of two things in that moment: that either I was not telling the truth, or she was going to pretend not be believe me to make it easier for herself.

She was not going to be letting this impact her life in any way. It was almost as if she had guessed what was coming.

I sat there and in that moment, it dawned on me how we look nothing alike. Our looks and modus operandi were completely opposite. She gave me a hug and said, 'I'm sorry' and left.

The therapist instantly voiced her concern at how much Kerry was willing to deny the information I was telling her. In particular, she was concerned she would do this as her children have been in his company and will continue to be.

I was dumbstruck. Kerry used to be good to me. When I first moved out of home she visited with spare food and toiletries supplies. She was maternal towards me.

I was good to her too and spent so much time with her family and babysitting for her. I had a brilliant relationship with my nieces and nephews. I adored them.

She always called me 'little sis.' It became clear to me that day that Kerry had *no idea* of the real meaning of sisterhood. I was devastated.

The final betrayal was from Mam. I had not heard from her in a month, since she had called to tell me the whole family were going to my aunt's house.

She informed me as if I was a neighbour and not a family member that I was not invited as it would be deemed

'Too much for you, the house will be too full, and you are pregnant.'

This aunt the 'golden alcoholic,' as Mam calls her, and

Kerry are close, and I imagine my not drinking probably made her uncomfortable. That combined with Mam or Kerry telling her I was not speaking to Ted was likely the real reason why I was excluded.

I contacted Ted to let him know I would go to family occasions if I so wished. The shame was on him and not me. He again tried to tell me I was crazy. Hyperventilating, I told him if he kept that tack up that I would tell everyone why I was refusing to be in his company.

I could tell from Dan and that call that Ted's approach was to continue to make out I was crazy. The implication came from Dan that they thought I was hormonal and pregnant, and this would pass after I had the baby.

At this time a call came from Mam to tell me,

'Ted told me what you said about him.'

'Oh okay.'

'What age were you?'

'I was nine.' There was silence. 'Do you believe me Mam?'

'Lucy, have you told Charlie's family?'

'Do you not believe me Mam?'

'I'm asking you have you told Charlie's family.'

'And I'm asking you do you believe me when I say he abused me?'

'No, I don't. But we can keep in touch.'

I had no words. There was more silence.

'Did you tell Charlie's family?'

'Look, Mam, I'm going to let you go now. I have to go here.'

I was too disappointed and annoyed to put her out of her misery and tell her Charlie's family did not know.

Mam phoned me the next day to say, 'I'm worried about you as a person.'

'Listen here *Mam,* don't phone me and put *my* character in question. I've had enough of Ted's *Lucy is crazy* bullshit and all you care about is if Charlie's family know.'

'Well, do they? Who have you told?'

'Jesus Christ almighty, Mam? There is no way I can tolerate any more of this crap at eight and a half months pregnant. He can continue to tell his lies and I will continue to tell the truth.' I hung up.

15

I prayed to let God guide me as to how to let go of them and to find further happiness. The tornado of blame from my family continued. My quiet determination to refuse to retract my words created a lot of noise from them. There were so many emotional pushes and pulls, then big smacks and whacks.

Occasionally I saw one coming. Most times I did not. I had no defence except to beg for mercy or to tell them I loved them. To say if they did not stop hurting me, I would have to stay away from them in some place they could not hurt me. I knew that would also hurt me too. There was so much hurt. Too. Much. Hurt.

I had to bunker down with all the things that would keep me grounded while the tornado passed. My recovery meetings, time with friends, counselling and talking to the homeopath helped me. Doing my gratitude list, meditating and having fun with Charlie and the girls kept me sane.

My three superpowers as I like to call them had to be practiced every day: mindfulness, gratitude, and belief in myself. I had to trust my higher power to keep me, Charlie, and our children protected.

Sometimes when I was back on my feet a swipe would come from nowhere and I was floored again. If I was half up, along came a blow and back down I went. I was battered and bruised beyond belief.

During that time, it took all my might to get out of bed. Putting on makeup became like a war paint ritual. I had a necklace gifted from friends that looked like a shield. I wore it for protection.

It had turned into a battle between them and me unnecessarily. I was so let down. For me it was about not wanting to be in Ted's company again and for all our children to be kept safe.

The emotional pain from being ousted from my family was akin to grief. At one point they pretended they were not having the annual anniversary mass for Shane and the get together afterwards with his friends.

Aunty Clare phoned me up and told me all about it after it was over. I was on my way to work. I was nearly crying. I was so hurt. I spontaneously phoned Mam, pleading for Ted and me to take turns at family occasions.

'Is there no way Ted and I can just take turns at family occasions? I am so hurt that you pretended not to have Shane's anniversary mass. What about me? He was my brother.'

Without warning, Ted started speaking on the phone. He must have been on the other line listening. I felt like I was going to crash the car. I revert to a young child when faced with him and young children are not able to drive.

Being on the motorway suddenly listening to him was a freaky experience. He tried to deny I had been excluded from any occasions,

'There is no reason you cannot visit.' He was putting on a feeble voice.

That aggravated me intensely. I knew Mam could hear him too and it was all a show. I could not listen to another second of his bullshit. I told him 'Get the fuck off this phone. I do not want to even hear your voice let alone see you. Give Mam back the phone. Now.'

Mam got back on the phone. I implored her, 'Mam, you can hear him lying down the phone to me; *you know* I have not been invited to the family occasions. *You know* why I cannot visit.'

She replied with her usual weak-willed nonsense. 'Lucy, maybe we can take turns.'

A switch flipped inside me. I suddenly saw Mam clearly. 'Why would I even want to be with people who treat me the way you have Mam? May God forgive you.'

I hung up.

I was shaking with white anger. I turned my car around and drove back towards home and straight to the Police station. I got there with a steely determination coursing through my mind and body.

It was so clear they were all going to Ted's house with their children. He sounded like he even believed his own lies now.

This was the reason I had told them all: to keep the children safe. The children were not safe if they were all pretending he did not do anything. They were all going along with or buying his lies. I did not know which was worse.

If I could not convince them of the truth over the previous two years, perhaps the police might. I sat in a small room at a metal table with a manky cup of tea. A lovely female sergeant sat with me and I told her I wished to report retrospective abuse.

Initially the sergeant suggested I come back another day and do it all on tape as they did not have the facilities to record me. She was going to be handwriting the statement out and explained that I had a better chance at prosecution if I was on tape.

I already knew that because there was no evidence, and he was denying everything that there would most likely be no prosecution. Strangely enough that is not what I wanted. I did not want Mam and my siblings to have to go through any more upset. I knew we were all hurting.

However, it was time he knew the game was over, thinking he was going to lie to my face and to imply to others I was crazy was over. If he knew I told the police, it might just scare him enough to make sure he did not do anything like that to any child again.

I refused to leave. I was not visibly upset or crying but I was embarrassed and stressed to be there. I did not want to be. I did not want it to be my reality let alone to have to share it with a stranger.

I was sacred how I would cope with the fallout of reporting Ted. The sergeant reassured me reporting the abuse was the right thing to do for myself and others. I explained to her that it took me over thirty years to get there and if I left that station that evening, I did not think I would go back. She agreed to take the statement.

She asked me many questions and stopped occasionally to offer me kind words. After five hours talking with that sergeant, I walked out of that building feeling like Ted no longer had any power over me. I handed him back the consequences of his bad behaviour. It was his problem now. It had been mine for too long.

The next day happened to be International Women's Day.

I ran around the garden with my two girls while we cheered, 'It's Women's Day, whoo hoo.' I was proud of myself for standing up to him. I hoped the girls would feel my strength and always stand up for themselves.

The real healing for me began. Like all emotional pain I tried to resist it, to outrun it, and to distract myself from it. All I could do was ride the waves of pain. I promised myself this was the last time I would have to heal from the hurt of my family.

The cycles of sadness, anger, dismay, distress, and disbelief I endured was almost unbearable. I had to go through it to come out the other side. Like an addict coming off heroine, there could not be one last hit, there was no last fix anymore. That could be the one that killed me.

Charlie reassured me, 'It's going to take time but it's going to be okay.'

I was blessed to have him and a sponsor like Marie. She never made me feel judged and always found the time to listen to me. From the start we clicked and became friends. She imparted her wisdom and all she learned over twenty years of sobriety in a graceful and kind way. I do not know how I would have gotten through the following months and years without Marie.

I remember arriving at a Dublin police station to give the second statement. I was like a fugitive and not in a fun way. My original statement was now transferred to the city of the 'crime', so I had to verify it by giving it again. That seemed so strange and a bit surreal.

I told myself I would spend time at the seafront while in Dublin, it had always been my sanctuary. Either when walking or cycling by the sea, during hangovers or when I was studying, it helped me clear my head.

I had my twenty-first in a bar there, many nights out, and meals there with friends. In early recovery it was a place I found peace. It was where Charlie and I had one of our first dates. It was my safe and happy place where I always manged to restore my equilibrium.

Despite everything, I was looking forward to having lunch there solo in my sanctuary after my appointment in the station. I hoped I would be clearing my head, feeling refreshed and grounded.

The reality was the opposite. Once I was done being interviewed with an emotionally unintelligent and unkind policeman I was upset. The way he spoke to me throughout the process made me feel like I was the person who did something wrong.

I needed and wanted to be back with Charlie as soon as possible. I had a knot in my stomach in case I met Kerry or Mam, even worse, if I was to see Ted.

I now felt like an imposter in my old sanctuary. I knew it should be ok for me to be there. Yet it was as if I was doing something wrong. I was wearing a long red coat, one I normally love. I felt I was wearing a flag that could reveal to the other side that I had crossed enemy lines. I did not feel safe. I was uneasy and fearful.

I no longer belonged around there. I was displaced from my land of origin. I had been identifying a lot with refugees, I even wrote a poem for them. I was empathising with their plight of having to leave the places they knew and loved and not being able to return for fear of attack or punishment. That was exactly how I felt.

I had to jump back into my car. I cried the whole way back to my own loving home. The safest one I have known. Thank God I have Charlie and my beautiful girls to live for. I belong with them.

It was almost impossible to weigh up which was most painful for me. Either seeing the people I loved and being hurt by them. Or not seeing the people I loved and being hurt by how much I missed them.

Paula and I had always been close. Eventually our telepathic connection seemed severed. A relationship can only withstand so much unresolved hurt.

I do not think Paula or me ever could have believed we would have been pushed so far apart. Ted fractured the family possibly beyond repair. For the previous two years I believed my family of origin did not understand what they were doing. I tried meditation to calm myself.

There were stressful phone calls with Dan. He continued to say he did not know who to believe. I repeatedly got off the phone, my face red with stress and upset. My chest and throat tight from not being able to say what I wanted to say, feeling it was not heard or understood.

He innocently relayed what Kerry and Mam were saying about me. They were not going to change their perspective or approach anytime soon. It hurt me deeply repeatedly.

I wrote letters to Mam and Kerry and I tried explaining but they ignored the letters and never wrote back. I came to realise they already knew how much they were hurting me by excluding me from all the family occasions and inviting Ted instead. They knew I was willing to do turn taking. They were not.

They knew what Ted did, but for some reason, they refused to admit it. Perhaps self-protection and their own pride or shame of not wanting to have to face reality. Even now, writing that, it is hard to breathe and swallow. It was devastating.

Brona, Aunty Clare and Uncle Brendan were not buying the lies from the others that I was not going to family occasions because I lived in a different county. They smelled the bullshit.

After all I had been at every family occasion for the previous thirty-six years. It took a lot of courage but eventually I told them. After being let down so badly by my family, I feared their reaction.

Brona was amazing, as always, she had my back and my hand one hundred percent. Uncle Brendan did too, he was rooting for me. I did not tell them I had reported him. I wanted Ted to find that out straight from the police. He needed a good fright to cop him on and out of his dangerously comfortable zone.

Over the following six months Aunty Clare never mentioned she had been told by Uncle Brendan. She called me every month telling me of a wedding anniversary or 'Ted's birthday party was lovely.'

I said I did not want to hear it. With a knot in my stomach, I said I would not keep pretending the elephant was not in the room. I asked her why she was choosing never to mention that she knew.

It was so new to me to speak so frankly and to stand my ground that I was shaking. She replied finding out had nearly caused her to have a nervous breakdown. She had cried and cried. She was so sad and dared not mention my name around them. I said I was sorry to hear I was now unmention-able and that she was pretending I did not exist to keep them comfortable.

She told me she loved me, she does, but she would not be getting involved. I said I loved her too. I do feel loved by her and my uncle. I understood that it was not easy for any of us.

As for the rest of my family, they all seemed to follow the same plan or pattern as it were. They had unwritten rules for the battle against Lucy's *'lies.'* Their *'make sure the truth never gets out'* strategy.

If you have been abused, you may recognise it. Most fam-ilies seem to instinctively and expertly know how to execute it. Relentlessly.

It will not matter what you say or do, before, during or after. They will proceed with the plan and the pain, even when it is hurting them too. Avoid her and the subject. Discuss anything else but never Ted or abuse. Blame her. It is all her fault we are all upset, and we will be angry with her. Stick together, come hell or high water. Deluded, remain deluded. Say she is deluded.

Twist everything, she has ever said or done, quickly make her out to be as crazy as possible. Lie if you have to. Do not ever admit you believe her. Exclude her. If the other plans do not work, then it is the only way.

The effect of avoiding and excluding me made me feel so unloved, unworthy, and uncared for.

The impact of them making their pain and lives more important than mine caused me frustration and a lot of anger. Their lack of empathy and the inability of them to actually support me was utterly devastating and nearly crushed me. The damage done by calling me deluded in their words and actions, caused me dismay and disbelief followed by rage.

I was there repeatedly for all of them in multiple ways for years. I was not a stranger. I was kind, loving and loyal to them. It seemed as if I meant absolutely nothing to them. I was as lonely as a person can possibly feel.

When I spoke to Marie, she always reminded me I was likeable and loveable, and they were the ones missing out. She did not suggest forgiving them but eventually she did encourage me to pray for them so I could 'detach with love.'

She explained how you cannot harbour ill feelings for others and feel free yourself. She also knew I had to say some *fuck you prayers* for them first before I could get to the point of wishing them well or detaching with love.

To exclude me meant rejecting my two beautiful girls too. That crushed me. I cried rivers over it. Even still I loved them. I did not get many loving acts in return.

Today I am aware that holding hurt, resentment, and anger towards them hurts me. I did not expect myself to forgive Ted, but I needed to try to forgive the rest of them for my own sake too.

Nelson Mandela said of those who imprisoned him, after release, he knew if he did not forgive them, he would remain a prisoner. He said there must be a long rest and much recovery

That could take the rest of my life to happen, but I had to try. I went to counselling. I resented having to find time and money to be there. I was tired of being hurt by other people.

Marie taught me I had to 'feel it to heal it' yet never in a wallowing or self-pitying way. People in recovery do not have the luxury of sitting on the 'Pity Potty.' That sort of thing can lead me back to a drink.

I had to shine a light on the pain. I had to explore all the dusty nooks and crannies of my mind and heart and give them a good spring clean until my inner house was clean and ready for living again.

Sounds easy. It is not. It is shit and hard and it hurts, and it is a lonely and painful road to travel. It brought me to my knees, but never for long.

I was determined I would be happy again. I seem to have a relentless sense of entitlement to a healthy and happy life. It has helped me pursue it for my family of four. I believe we deserve it, and we can have it. Why not? Life is a blessing to be rejoiced in.

I willed my life to distract me into my now. I practiced being in each moment. The less I tried to make my truth understood, the more I began to understand and accept it myself.

I emerged stronger and wiser until I felt myself like the red Varanogi woman I had seen flying in the sky, embodying my freedom, power, and peace. I think the vision I had while meditating on the retreat almost eight years previously was something deep within me trying to expand.

I was escaping from all those years of being pushed down by alcohol and being a chameleon. Now I was inhabiting my being. I was integrated and this part of me was not something that was going to evaporate again.

Christmas rolled around shortly after Hope's birth. We were feeling blessed and besotted. Everything outside our home was wonderfully white.

I held Joy's chubby little toddler hand in mine while we went exploring in our winter wonderland. She shrieked whenever the snow crunched under her little boots. We stayed out until we were numb from the tops of our fingers to the tips of our toes.

Upon return I tapped the front of my boot before I entered our home, feeling so grateful for our beautiful home. The luxury of leaving the ice behind me and having a loving place to go.

Charlie scooped Joy up into his arms while the heat of our wood fire enveloped me. I picked up Hope, the cosy bundle from her crib and pressed my cheek against her mini cheek. She generously shared her warmth and her milky breath. It was delightful.

I told her how a week before she was born the nearby lane was overflowing with flowers called baby's breath. She looked at me, her bright eyes aglow. We leaned our foreheads together with our eyes gently fixed on each other. I felt we already knew the other.

As we sat there, I lost all sense of time, besotted with her tiny fingers and teeny toes. They were the smallest I had ever seen. I kissed her pixie nose. At six weeks old my love and my light was shining brightly at me, equalled by her big sister Joy.

I stayed up late with Hope that night, relishing every precious moment. I knew she would need at least three feeds in the night. There would be cuddles and nappy changes too and I felt privileged to be her mam.

In my life there are some moments I will never forget. That night as Hope lay on my chest both her tiny feet fitted into one of my hands. I was in awe of her and her whole life ahead of her to be lived, to evolve from such a tiny, beautiful bundle and how magical she already was.

I longed for my own mam and my sisters. They were all mammies too. I wanted them to witness my marvellous girls, all the concerning and the glorious moments. I shared them with other mammy friends.

We had a christening for our gorgeous Hope. I missed my family not being there. I worried that Mam might pass away unexpectedly and suddenly like Shane.

16

To love, to be loved and to learn to love myself are the greatest blessings and lessons of my life. Sometimes love alone cannot sustain a person. You need to rest and replenish too.

Yes, love is the thing that can survive after death. I hope to live a very long life before I leave a legacy of love behind me.

More recently I had my own brush with death. Thanks be to the Lord or Buddha or whichever great spiritual beings that look after me out there I had my very own private resurrection. It happened unannounced, quickly and quietly. Yet on hindsight it had been coming for months. I was experiencing a sore throat, swallowing and speaking hurt.

I went back and forth to my doctor and without examination we repeatedly put it down to my sinuses. Chronic sinusitis and night-time mouth breathing was apparently causing the dry and sore throat. Lovely.

Chocolate causes me to get sinusitis. On the tough days Minstrels, Dairy Milks, and white chocolate Magnum ice creams picked me up. They helped me put on a happy face and to fake it until I could make it. I wondered how much longer it was going to take.

It was over two years since I confronted Ted and refused to be in his company any longer. It was over one year since I told the rest of the family how much ostracizing me hurt but to no avail. I needed to move on now. I was so tired of it not being over for me mentally and emotionally. I had a theory of my own as to why I kept getting sick, not to be shared with my doctor.

Speaking my truth was possibly painful for me. Due to a lack of support, I felt like I had no voice in my family of origin. At least not one that was being heard.

The lack of communication, understanding or support from the rest of the family was shocking to me. I did not want to ever see or hear from Ted again. But I felt brushed under the carpet, by the rest of them, trampled on and forgotten.

I was squashed and crumpled, and it was taking me so long to bounce back to full form. Charlie was angry at what he perceived to be a lack of backbone of support from my siblings. As far as everyone else was concerned I believed I had to act like nothing was going on. I kept it private from everyone because I was ashamed that my 'family' ostracized me.

It was a difficult place for me to be on a daily basis. I was convinced I should not tell people I was grieving for a family who were alive. To me it was as devastating as if there had been a high-speed crash on the motorway involving a pile up and each car was full of people I love.

My siblings, their children, my sister in-law, my brother in-law and my aunts and uncles. I woke up crying some nights after dreaming I was reunited with Kerry's children, my nieces and nephews. I missed them desperately. I worried that they would not know how much I loved them because I did not see them.

I had to stay away so I could heal and be a good mam to my girls. I focused on all the things I was grateful for and there was a lot. Every night I wrote down a long gratitude list and every morning I recalled the list in my head. I finally understood fully why Marie repeatedly told me, 'A grateful alcoholic won't drink, Lucy you must maintain an attitude of gratitude.'

She was right, doing this helped me get up and to keep on going. Despite the hurt I was going through I still managed to notice and enjoy all the positive in my day and life.

I knew Mam and my siblings loved me, but I was devastated they were willing to cut me off. They were missing out on my girls being in their lives. I kept going. I kept putting my best side out and practicing my gratitude.

I militantly focused on all the positive in my life. It was the armour I had in this battle. I wanted to be happy. I had so much to be happy about. I was hurting deeply. It was exhausting trying so hard to be ok with it and to not let it get me down. It was also not possible. It took so much from me.

It was a god damn emotional marathon. I had no road map and no training to prepare me either. I did not even know anyone else who ran the same road to turn to for advice.

Eventually it took its toll on me on every level. It was a Thursday evening and unseasonably warm for the end of April. We were visiting a friend of Charlie's who was not long out of hospital and recovering from cancer.

I felt exhausted and a bit achy. Compared to undergoing the treatment that his friend was experiencing I was, 'Fine, good, tired, yeah sure I'm grand thanks.' *Nothing to see here.* I grew accustomed to feeling rough like that on and off. I reverted to being the chameleon when I needed to. I had perfected that trick of pulling out whatever mask I needed during my drinking career.

I could transform my pained face into a happy one. I was even starting to fool myself. So, I did not pay it much attention to the fact that I was yet again feeling unwell and claiming to feel fine.

The visit was over. We plucked the girls off the trampoline, said goodnight and off we went. Normally within minutes of arriving home we would be milling around making dinner, changing a nappy, throwing on a wash, feeding kids, getting them to bed, tidying up and collapsing on the chair.

Often Charlie and I competed in a game of who was the most tired. We compared sleep apps to see who had the most minutes sleep the night before or who was going to get up first that night.

The children shouted out for us at night for drinks, snacks, cuddles, to get into our bed or to request that we sing songs for them.

Unbeknownst to himself, Charlie was going to be flying solo. He found me sitting on the couch snuggling my hot water bottle, shivering. This behaviour was unheard of since he knew I prided myself on being a bit of a work horse. *Stupid fucking pride.*

On this particular evening my Charlie was wide-eyed with curiosity and concern to see me firstly sitting down in the middle of the bedtime routine. Secondly, I was quivering on the chair, pale, clutching the hot water bottle. I did not feel right at all. 'I feel like my whole body is being attacked. I'm in pain everywhere.'

The Easter break from work had commenced for us both that day. My first holidays from work since Christmas.

Charlie reassured me 'It's probably that thing that happens

230

where you're really busy, when you finally get a break, you feel like crap.'

'Yeah, probably love.' It hurt to talk. I went to bed early and I woke up feeling sicker. The next day I was in even worse shape. My throat was very tight, and swallowing felt like hot water on a burn. This was more than being tired.

I was not able to swallow the painkillers anymore. They were getting stuck, and I was half choking and coughing them up. Charlie and I texted even though we were in the same room as it was too sore for me to talk.

I was in agony. My face and lips were swollen now too. I went to Caredoc, they said I had a virus and sent me home. This felt worse than a virus, so I phoned Caredoc back and spoke to another doctor.

I said I did not feel right and asked was there anything else I could do. I was advised to gargle soluble painkillers and maybe try suck some cough sweets. Having not slept for three nights I wanted to tell this new doctor where to stick a sweet.

I rasped out 'I'm in severe pain, a cough sweet is not going to cut it.'

'The level of pain does not equal the level of illness you are experiencing.' The doctor informed me.

'I'm crying in pain. I did not even cry like this after my caesarean sections, and they were bloody sore.'

'Gargle some more Disprin' was the solution.

I sat up on the couch, crying on and off and waiting for Charlie and the girls to wake up. They woke up at 7am and by 7.30am we were on our way to the Accident and Emergency department.

I hugged and kissed the girls goodbye. Charlie promised as soon as he got a minder for them, he would come back to me. In I went and pretty soon I was on the other side of the triage section. I was examined and blood tests were taken. Various nurses and doctors asked me questions. They had an almost puzzled look at me.

There was no going back outside for me now. I was in a room, in a bed, my tired and pained face looking at a consultant's worried face. He advised me that the ear nose and throat specialist was in another hospital and that they may need to send me there.

Charlie arrived and he answered all the same questions. When the doctor asked, 'Any dribbling?' I whispered 'no' feeling like my dignity was at stake, even though I was spitting out my saliva into a paper bowl. It was not possible to swallow at all. My throat was nearly closed.

Charlie raised his eyebrows at me, 'Lucy you were dribbling last night.' He said it loud enough for the consultant to hear him. Charlie was not going to let me minimise my symptoms.

He looked from him to me with an expression that asked, well, is it true, you do indeed dribble? I nodded in agreement, feeling found out, yet still very calm because I had full faith in the doctors' ability to de-dribble me.

They observed me on and off for less than an hour. Charlie had to go and relieve the child minder. Straight after he walked out of the room the consultant walked back in and said,

'Lucy, you are going to the other hospital right now via ambulance. There are too many concerning factors.'

'Can we wait two minutes while I phone Charlie to come back, please?' I started rustling around for my phone. The doctor stopped me, 'No. There is no time for that, he can meet you there.' It was my first trip in an ambulance. I was slightly disappointed to observe that inside it was the same as a converted bus.

I phoned Charlie and we both said how it was surreal that I was phoning him while I was flying down the motorway in an ambulance. I had no idea how ill I was. He promised to get to me as quickly as possible. The minder could not take the children back until 6pm.

I was a little mortified to be carted into the next hospital in a wheelchair. The paramedics left me with the triage nurse who took me straight to the ear nose and throat department. As I transferred to the specialist consultant's chair for examination my legs wobbled.

She was a beautiful foreign woman her English was direct. After close examination and lots of questions she advised me, 'We don't know what is wrong here yet, we need to do an MRI scan. This could potentially be life-threating; you should call your husband.' I sat there numb for a minute.

I told myself, *English is not her first language. She doesn't mean that. Sure, I'm fine. It's another sore throat. I'm run down probably.*

My second thought came like a massive slap. *Jesus Christ she can't mean that.* I started to cry. She looked at me and said, 'So you will go for the MRI now, and someone will come to collect you in a minute.'

'Yeah, ok, but I thought you said this might be life-threatening and I might die?'

She came up, stood in front of me, looked me in the face and eyes, 'Yes, this could be life-threating Lucy.'

I was crying even more now and asked, 'But if it got too bad surely you can do something?' I was thinking *I'm in the hospital, with you, the specialists and the equipment and modern medicine. Surely you can fix me, can't you?*

'You are in the right place, Lucy,' was her reply. She was offering no promises and no reassurance that I was going to be ok.

I sat there crying for a couple of minutes. She returned and asked me, 'Is your mobile phone working? Do you need the hospital phone to call your husband?'

I whispered 'no.' I was trying to compose myself before I called him. I explained, 'Charlie, they are saying it is serious. Can you get here any quicker than 6pm?'

'I'll try love, but I don't think so.' I knew he would be there as soon as possible. All I ever had to do was want him there, let alone need him and he would be there in a flash.

I did not want to fill him full of fear and for him to speed down the road and crash the car on the motorway. The two kids would have no parents. Christ, dying was not an option.

Off I went, in shock. I had the MRI. They used the intravenous dye. I have a needle phobia and I get very scared if I have to have one. I was too numb from shock and pain to be concerned about the injection.

Afterwards I was taken to an area in the emergency department. Two nurses watched me, and the consultant circled around my bed checking on me. They gave me three antibiotics intravenously and steroids.

The consultant came back and advised me that the MRI scan showed an infection under my tongue inside my neck. I could not stop thinking of what she said.

She told me the anaesthetist would be there soon to meet me. He would be on standby because I may need a tracheotomy but there was no guarantee that would work.

She left and I started to cry again. I did not even fear the tracheotomy, not one tiny bit. I feared it not succeeding in its purpose.

When you are faced with the possibility of dying, you will take anything above it. Once it's living. I thought to myself, *I must live. I did not survive being held hostage in the hut and killing Ted to die now.*

A kind-looking male nurse came over busying himself with all the tubes beside me that I was actually not tied to. He saw I was crying and on my own in a shit and scary situation. 'Are you ok? Is there anything I can do for you?'

'Is it possible I could I die here? From this?' I was barely audible.

He replied, 'You are in the right place.' There it was, that statement again. The one that offers no comfort.

I had to clear it up immediately. Holding back tears and fear, I asked him 'Seriously, if this doesn't work, there is other stuff you can do?'

He sat down on the bed. His expression told me he was going to level with me. 'Well, you see, Lucy, your tongue, your throat, your tonsils, your oesophagus and your epiglottis are all so severely swollen that we cannot promise if the antibiotics don't reduce the swelling that a tracheotomy will even work for you.'

Tears of disbelief rolled off my face onto my t-shirt. I made no attempt to stop them. I was in shock. He offered those words again, 'You are in the right place Lucy.'

As I nodded, I was now not so convinced there was a right place for me and my infection. Tears continued to fall out of my eyes. Off he went. I can see him walking away in his lilac scrubs.

I can see myself too in that hospital bed. Suddenly with my life in question. In that moment I became the clearest I had ever been in my whole life.

I laid back propped up on the hospital pillows and told myself. *No. No way. Not today. Today I do not die. Not seeing my daughters growing up is not an option. It cannot happen. I will not let it happen. I have too much to live for. No, not today. Today I live. I must live.*

I closed my eyes and took deep breaths. I visualised the gentlest pink imaginable, candy floss clouds surrounding my throat, my head and my neck.

I told myself and my body over and over, *this swelling will go down, my throat will get well. I am willing this visualisation and this medicine to work. I allow this medicine to work. I will be well. I will be well. I am alive and I am staying alive. I am.*

It was the most sober I have ever been in my life. I am sure there was noise and bustle. I was silent and still in an almost meditative state and it soothed me.

I sensed Jesus was on one side of me and Shane was on the other. I was all alone, but yet I was not. Jesus being there was unexpected for me. I told him where to go when I was fourteen. Now I realise maybe he never left. I possibly built a wall that he waited on the other side of.

The next few hours are a blur. I know by 6pm Charlie was by my side, of course, my gorgeous husband. The doctor advised us that the antibiotics and steroids were taking effect. I was most likely, according to them going to be okay.

As far as I was concerned, I was most definitely going to be okay. It was Easter time and I joked with Charlie 'If Jesus rose from the dead this time all those years ago, then it's my turn now.'

He humoured me, 'Yes, it is love.'

Maybe it was the steroids or maybe I was happy to be alive.

They moved me to the intensive care unit. I thought it unnecessary, as far as I was concerned sure I was grand, on the mend. That night is hazy too.

The next day I was moved to a normal ward. I believed I was home and dry. I missed my girls more than words can say.

I was high on steroids and when the pain killers wore off, I was in agony. I was alive and so bloody grateful to be. I did not have my parents and siblings visiting like other patients, but I did have my Charlie. That was enough for me, my rock-solid husband. I know it cannot have been easy for him.

I was in touch with my good friends too. I am grateful for the fabulous friends I have. I realised my body mimicked what my mind felt. I lost my voice and my body was not going to let me forget it.

Out of nowhere I heard my usual friends in the spirit world and the unexpected one, the big JC. They were telling me, *Lucy, you are strong. We are here to remind you who you are. You are enough. You are lovable and you do belong here on this earth.*

I decided in the hospital that whatever does not make me happy I will not do it anymore. I realised my life is not going to last forever, even though I wish it would.

Within days of that experience while still in the hospital I emailed my boss. I requested to reduce my hours to three days a week. It was approved.

Things had to change. It was five long days before I got to hug my girls in a hospital corridor. Every morning I asked the consultant and his team, 'Can I go home to my girls today? I'll rest up there.'

The answer was, 'Not yet, Lucy.'

They checked me over and put a camera down the back of my nose daily to look at my throat. That was stressful and uncomfortable. They had to make sure the infection was completely under control before they let me go.

The ward I was on was not suitable for children to visit. Eventually I was allowed to meet with them in the café. It was like Christmas. It was too long to wait for them and too short a time with them.

I hugged Charlie so tight too. I vowed to be extra grateful every single day, to slow down and get well. The team kept a close eye on me. My infection markers measured by blood tests were supposed to be in the normal range of fifteen. When I arrived at the hospital, they were at one hundred and thirty two.

For the first two days they remained dangerously high and so was my blood pressure. I was pumped full of antibiotics and steroids and on the third day I improved. I was indeed rising from the dead.

At that time, I spoke to a family member on the phone and after I hung up I lay there flummoxed. I had the old familiar feeling of the floor falling away from under me, ungrounded, unsafe and again unloved.

I could not believe they had seemed so uncaring on the call. If I found the will to be compassionate to them through all of this, why could they not afford me the same? Even to at least to treat me with the respect that I deserved.

Charlie came to visit me that evening. I was drained, my health was deteriorating again. I barely felt able to get out of the bed. I cried with him and we went to the hospital church and lit a candle together.

I said a prayer asking for healing for my family and also from the hurt at the hands of my family of origin yet again.

That evening after Charlie left and the next day, I was very unwell again. I was getting worse instead of better. When the team did their daily morning check on me, they advised me that my infection markers had gone back up and so had my blood pressure. This was after the upsetting call.

In case I was unsure, the universe was showing me how my family of origins behaviour was literally making me sick. I had suspected that for a while. There was no meaningful contact from Mam or Kerry. They say people are not good or bad, they are both. I had to face that reality and make greater changes.

After one week I got to go home. Joy gave me a gift of a small wooden house, a half-moon kind of crooked fairy house. Before I got sick, we bought it together and we painted it red with one small green window. I knew every time I saw that half-moon house it would remind me of what I had learned. What I needed to do and as importantly to not do, to stay well.

I have it beside me as I write, and I look at it often. After an almost unbearable amount of pain, to stay well and sane,

I had to cut contact with the people that were hurting me: some of my family of origin. It made me so sad. I never wanted to have to make that decision. It seemed incredible to me to be in this position.

All the old feelings of grief and sadness of saying goodbye to Shane again were back and worse in a way, as they were all alive.

Ted was still insisting to the family I was lying and implying I was crazy. The more I protested I was not, I felt I was looking and almost going crazy. He was driving a gap between the rest of the family and me.

I began to detach from them. I spoke the truth, and this was my way of protecting myself now. I broke the unhealthy and dysfunctional chain and cycle forever.

My children will never know such a crazy world. We can be well and happy and our true selves. We can live our lives happily and peacefully without any unwell or negative energy dragging us down.

It took weeks of antibiotics and appointments with cameras put down my nose and throat repeatedly, but I got well again.

I do many things to stay well. That includes constantly looking out for and listening to the people living empowered lives full of courage and wisdom. I have been doing that for years now.

I hear people in recovery meetings, at work and I find them online. I read their books and learn from their research and experience. This helps me to stay really well, and I believe to evolve in mind and spirit too.

Recently I thought about how I had jokingly likened my healing experience to the resurrection. When I delved a little deeper it was because I felt had been crucified by some of my family of origin.

I got pondering on what it was Jesus said when he was actually on the cross *Forgive them for, they know not what they are doing.* These words came into my mind, heard long ago at school.

I asked myself: *have I forgiven my family of origin? Can I forgive them on the basis that they know not what they are doing?* The answer: *I do my best to accept them as they are while protecting myself from any more hurt.*

Over time and reflection, I can see we are all the product of our environment. We are the sum of the knowledge, skills and coping tools we have in a moment. Not just our choices and reactions.

That has helped me greatly to heal and let go of the hurt. Of course, there are scars that is ok, I earned them by loving people.

Today I choose not to be around people who hurt me. I cannot have them in my life while they still operate from their own place of pain.

Unfortunately, hurt people can and often do hurt other people. A relationship can only survive a certain amount of hurt. Especially when it is repeatedly unresolved and unacknowledged whether it is intentional or not.

Back when I shared with them about what Ted did, I was operating from a place of deep and raw pain too. I did not always get it right. I did not always manage to spare people's feelings. Even when I was trying my best.

Marie has mentioned many times to 'Give people the right to be wrong.'

I can do that and I can extend that notion to myself too. I can wish them well and pray they find their own way to heal. I do hope it happens in my life time.

17

I focus on lavishing as much love as humanly possible on my true loves. That is not difficult as they are the easiest beings to love, and they make my world shine brightly.

I returned to part-time work, now a mam of two. To my own surprise, despite sleep deprivation and baby brain I even progressed at work. Another six months zipped by in a haze of late nights and early mornings.

During the school term, Charlie and I whizzed by each other often during the night too. We were yo-yoing in and out of the girls' rooms during the night. Neither were great sleepers yet. Another Christmas was on the way. We were all very excited.

I saw mothers shopping with their daughters and grand-children. Every café seemed to have siblings sharing coffee and chats. I stopped my heart from sinking too low by think-ing of my world of love in my home. I was determined to maintain my gratitude for all the joy and love in my life.

I was in touch with Dan, it was somewhat strained. He maintained he believed Ted when he was with him and me when he was with me. I knew Ted was twisting his brain with his lies. I was hurt and worried for him.

We arranged a Christmas visit to Dan's with him. I had fun carefully choosing gifts for his children. He had a family of his own now too. I bought them a fishing rod set for the bath, com-plete with floating pretend poo. It was good wholesome child-like humour. I figured Dan and I would get a kick from it too.

I hoped we would have a chuckle and that the children would run around together. I would still have my little brother in my life. I could consider myself not completely cut off and unloved by my family of origin.

A call came from Dan. Our visit was cancelled. One of his children was sick. There were no rearrangements for a Christmas visit in place. He was the only family member I was in touch with.

I heard from a mutual family friend that Kerry had been spilling poison and she had his ear. Telling the truth was making them uncomfortable and I was not going to be let away with that.

I was falling down into a hole again and I had to find a way not to hit the bottom. I kept breathing and returning to my gratitude list in my head.

Charlie and our gorgeous girls are always at the top and our wonderful life. I did my very best not to let this keep me down. For a while I succeeded. I parked the past and I was present for every element of my luscious life.

That Christmas, Charlie and I had the beautiful gift of time with our loves. We delighted in the girls well wrapped up with their peachy cheeks and squishy smiles. By evening we were happy when their bedtime came for us time.

After Christmas I was putting away the decorations. To be exact, I was repacking Charlie's gallant efforts. He seemed oblivious of the fact that Hope's laminated elf face peering out from the oversized Santa Claus hat has to be securely packed away.

That and all other manner of special memories must be

treated as precious gems. Nothing about these magical moments with my loves can ever be forgotten.

The taking down of the decorations was done and dusted but I did not get the usual glow of satisfaction I normally get.

Instead, I was made uneasy by the presence of the neat pile of presents, wrapped with love that were left behind the couch. When I went to pull the curtains, my heart was tugged by the fun we were not having. I wanted us to be fishing for poo or to hear the giggling over the book that had the farting buttons.

The cushion for Dan and his wife no longer looked plump; it seemed odd and misplaced. Dan's fashionably fitted shirt had not even seen a festive party. They all sat there, untouched, reminding me that for the first time in forty years I had not seen or even had a conversation with any of my family of origin over Christmas.

The tears came and I sobbed. My heart hurt. I got myself together. I bundled up Joy and Hope and the gifts and we posted them off with well wishes to Dan and his family.

Joy did not understand why we were not taking them to their house. I did. After some weeks the silence was broken with a thank you text from Dan's wife. I guessed he was likely resentful at me because he believed I ruined Christmas. The anger that should have been directed at Ted was misplaced onto me.

I got good at concealing tears at home and in work. Grief does not respect time, places or mascara. An old song that used to be a favourite now reduced me to tears in an instant.

Memories of being at a gig or a night out with Dan and Paula made me so lonely for the good times we had. There were reminders everywhere of all my siblings, Mam and my nieces and nephews.

I even went through that phase I experienced after Shane died where I kept thinking I saw them. At times I thought I saw one of them in a crowd or in the distance at a gig. Grief plays cruel tricks on the mind.

Music for me has always been one of the quickest portals to a time, place or feeling. I struggle to listen to Elvis now. If he comes on the radio, I turn it off.

As I was growing up Ted used to play Elvis. We all danced. We took turns standing on the dining room table while he danced with us.

I believe no one person is all good or all bad. I think that applies to Ted too. It is tricky to find a place in my mind or heart for my happy memories of him. It feels too strange for me to still care about him and some of the things associated with him.

Yet simultaneously to dislike him and those same things associated with him. He has caused me so much torment. I resent Ted and the fact that Elvis and so much more fills me with so much conflicting emotions.

I am learning to accept that relationships, fractured ones, are not straightforward. I cannot change that.

Christmas without any contact from Mam made me miss her too. I longed for a mam in my life. Maybe I always will. Not being mothered creates a want and a need that is hard to heal.

It frustrates me that this is the case no matter what age I am. I nurture myself; it has taken time to figure out what I need. I have to stop if I do not feel right and check *what do I need?*

Sometimes I will not realise I am hungry until I feel shaky or get a headache. It is like the connections in my brain misfire. It does not always come natural for me to love and look after myself, but I am learning.

I can look at one of my girls or hear them cry in another room and know exactly what they need. I am grateful I have a natural mothering instinct and I love it.

I am also so pleased that I finally realise pain is not to be avoided. I cannot take the pain out of life. I became resilient by going through certain experiences and negative emotions and by being vulnerable and honest with people who cared about me and how much I was hurting.

Not by avoiding the feelings. I no longer need to shelter my girls from every danger I can possibly perceive and predict. I can teach them and tell them every day: 'You are strong, you are brilliant, you are brave, and you are clever, and it is ok to feel however you feel.'

I recently heard Hope, who is only a toddler, talking to herself. Her playdough was on the floor under her small table. While she was trying to squish under it, I overheard her say, 'I can do this. I can do this. I can do this.'

She did not look to me to do it; she did not cry. She had self-belief. Wow. I am so happy Charlie, and I can instil self-esteem and self-worth in our girls. You either have it or you do not. My girls have it in bucket loads, in fact, their buckets overflow.

I phoned Dan. I mentioned that I missed Mam and I was very hurt by the exclusion from the family occasions by her and Kerry.

He said he did not want to hear it, certainly not right then and there. They had all spent Stephen's Day together. I knew it was becoming increasingly hard for him to keep a foot in each camp: theirs and mine.

I was ostracized. I was the dying member in a jungle tribe who is brought outside on a stretcher and left as far away as possible, so the group do not have to see and hear the pain or smell as the person rots to death. I was never going to be brought back in. They had to kill me off, but at what cost.

For a short while after that I felt I was losing my mind, again. In the week that followed Hope did not sleep for five nights in a row. Friends told me the full moon had their children up too.

During those nights and days my mind was regularly invaded by negative voices droning on at me. They banged on every inch of my brain over and over, a low chubby thud that could not be ignored.

It disturbed most of my moments. Their voices were those of my family of origin. The cruellest words that had come my way over the previous two years, as they picked my life and character apart.

It took all my will not to break. Not to freak the fuck out and do something crazy. It is a miracle I did not turn back to my old friend alcohol. I knew there was no solution in a bottle of cider.

I went into recovery meetings for my drinking, and I had to stay for my thinking. These intrusive thoughts hurt me over and over. I wondered how much hurt one soul could take.

Usually, I reverted to my mindfulness and gratitude to realign my mind, body, and spirit if I was struggling. My unwavering optimism that I always managed to hold on to for forty years was no longer eternal.

Oh no, this was now real and raw, and I knew what I had to do. This was getting serious now. I had to find a way to forgive them fully, somehow.

I refused to die inside and going crazy was not an option either. I prayed to Shane. I had to trust he was with me and my friends in the spirit world and that I could get through this.

This was not the same as the emergency praying, I did for many years because I wanted something. This was a cry out to a force much bigger than me for help.

I prayed harder than I have ever prayed. I wanted to be able to let my family of origin go or to forgive them. Or to not be so god damn angry.

I do not have the words for how angry I was. I was raging. Three months after Hope's christening, Kerry sent her a letter. Hope was ten months old. It was passive-aggressive and bitchy towards me.

It was a couple of months after my fortieth birthday; Kerry included a serenity angel with the letter for me. I ran out to the garden and smashed that angel off the wall. *Who the fuck did she think she was?*

I was getting used to stifling screams. Ted was adding insult to injury by turning Mam and my siblings against me with his lies.

Marie understood why I was so angry, but she warned me, 'Lucy we don't have the luxury of anger; even if it's justified it can drive us back to drink.'

'I know, I just can't believe they are letting me down this

bloody badly. I really hurt my foot kicking the wall I'm just so angry.'

'Lucy, there has to be no more fuck you all rages or kicking the wall. That just ends up hurting you too.'

I cried quietly on the other end of the phone. 'I have to try to forgive my mam and my siblings, don't I? I'm lost as how to do that.'

'I know you are confused and frustrated. Try punching the bed instead. You can try saying a prayer for them, even if initially the prayer is a fuck you one.'

'No matter how hard I try it seems impossible to reconcile the situation or to let them go.'

'Perhaps you can pray for the willingness to both forgive them and let them go.'

'Yeah, maybe. I just wish it was different and that this was a bad dream I could wake up from.'

I went back to counselling, my homeopath, the process worker had moved away. I found a new local person. In one hour, at high speed I tried to explain what was going on.

As I was leaving, she rummaged in a drawer and gave me a slip of paper with a definition saying: 'Forgiveness is different from condoning, excusing, pardoning, forgetting, and reconciliation.'

I was fed up with all the wise words. I wanted to know how to go about it. The following session I told her so. She suggested, 'Sit with your feelings. Where is your chance to fall apart in all of this?'

Fall- a- fucking -part. I did not have the time, interest or energy to fall apart. I had been there done that. It was a risky business.

This was the putting the Lucy who fell off the wall back together part. *Sit with it?* That may be good advice for some people, but not me.

I could not decipher how I felt. I wanted to feel different. I was desperate to feel properly peaceful again.

I continued to talk to Marie about this notion that forgiving those who hurt me would bring me peace. I could experience deep inner calm and I would feel completely integrated again. I told her I was worried that it was possibly a 'Bullshit, wishful thinking conclusion to come to?'

'No, Lucy, you are only fooling yourself by thinking you will be okay carrying around all that hurt. It's like taking poison and hoping the other person dies.'

'Marie, I'm past the wanting to kill people phase of all of this, I think.'

'Well, that's good. I can't afford to bail you out.'

We always managed a chuckle among all the serious stuff.

'Take the programme serious but don't take yourself too seriously.'

Marie was right.

I wanted to be calm enough to say a prayer for them and for myself. I was tired of it all. I needed for it to be over and for it to be ok. That looked unlikely. Marie helped me to understand that I had to start with getting my peace of mind back and to enjoy all the good I had in my life.

'How on earth am I going to get from the rage to reverence?'

She reminded me to say the serenity prayer. 'Remember this when you do not know what to do, do nothing. Say the serenity prayer: "God grant me the serenity to accept the things I cannot change. The courage to change the things I can and the wisdom to know the difference".'

This sounds simple but it is not. Doing nothing is the hardest thing for me to do. I am a born, shaped, and professionally trained fixer. I pride myself on being 'solution-focused.' I love a good schedule and a planner and a to-do list. That is when I am in my comfort zone.

All the new counsellor's advice of 'riding it out,' 'waiting it out,' 'let it unfold,' 'trust your higher power'—they have been my biggest challenges. I just do not like doing all that.

I really do not want to have to 'sit with' negative emotions. I prefer to be getting on, getting over, getting under or getting out of it.

Instead, I had to not do anything unhealthy to numb the pain or at least distract myself from it. I learned I have to go through pain, to transform, and to come out the other side.

Loving myself no matter what has to be a priority. I reverted to my gratitude list in my mind whenever I could. That created good feelings.

I put a note on my mirror in saying 'what other people think of me is none of my business. I love me.' It was time to act as if until I became as if, *again*.

I had to rewire parts of my brain which is no small task. It is like trying to get up every day and brush your teeth, make your tea, and eat your breakfast with your left hand, except you are right-handed so it is difficult.

You forget and use the wrong hand. It does not come easily but it is possible after a lot of practice and reminders. I slowly but surely calmed down.

I began to relax into not doing anything with the tough

feelings except to ride them out. It really was like giving up an addiction all over again.

Extracting myself from a dysfunctional family dynamic felt all wrong on an emotional level. It was all I knew so I wanted to stay.

It was like thinking alcohol was my friend when in reality it was messing up my mind and my life. Sick people make me sick, even if I am related to and I love them.

I came to learn what being from a dysfunctional family meant. Apparently dysfunctional means operating in a place of pain. If you are in this type of family and all the layers of dynamics are up and running for years, it is not possible to be yourself.

Mam contacted me out of the blue a couple of years into being ostracized. After a few minutes of her acting like we just talked the day before I asked her 'Are you ready to talk about why I was ostracized from the family? Why you and Kerry essentially kicked me out of the family? You know you didn't have to choose? It didn't have to be me or him.'

'I know. I suppose we just let it slide.' That was her response. *Slide?*

'So, you thought you would just let your daughter *slide* out of your life? Even after we lost Shane you were ok to lose me too, because you don't believe me about him?' I asked.

'I believe he is innocent Lucy. I think you imagined it; you took it up wrong.' She said those words to me.

'Don't dare say that to me. I didn't imagine anything, and which one is it? either I imagined it or I took it up wrong? I can't have done both. I also don't believe that you think I imagined it. That would make me unwell, which I'm not and if I was, then what kind of mother would that make you?' There was silence.

I had to finally say it 'I would never treat my girls how you have treated me. You have not been a mother to me or a grandmother to them.'

'I miss the kids.' She was being ridiculous now.

'They don't know who you are, you met Hope once.' I somehow stayed calm.

'At least I met her once.'

'If you think that's ok. If you think telling me I'm imagining him abusing me or he did something that I took up wrong, trying to make it my fault and that excluding me from the family is ok then I'm not sure what you want from me.' I just actually wanted her to leave me alone now.

'I don't feel great Lucy. I have to go.'

'Yes, that's always been your way to avoid having a backbone.'

'Goodbye Lucy.'

'Yeah bye.'

This was my experience. Every time I engaged with them, they took me back to a place of pain. I had to get back up one last time and this time I stopped going back. It was as hard as giving up an addiction.

It was painful, intense, and I did not know who I was or could be without them. *Was it possible to be happy if my family of origin did not love and include me anymore?* I found it very hard to convince myself it was even a possibility.

I came to realise they did love me. They were in too much pain to face any more. The truth was too painful for them. That was their problem and I had to leave it with them. I tried everything and repeatedly got nowhere.

Once I got to that point I started to move forward again and to stop looking back so much. I slowly saw my worth again.

My children love and need me that helped me to love myself again. I was now willing and not wanting to try to forgive my family of origin. I saw they were as sick as the secret they were so desperately trying to keep.

Staying angry would be the same as getting back into that hut of hurt I escaped from in the desert.

Despite all the crap I came from I created a beautiful life and a healthy family of my own. I faced the truth. I told the truth. That took greater courage than killing a tiger.

I am free to be me, and it is amazing. Finally at forty-years-old I am able to dance like myself and not worry who sees me. During my teens and twenties, I had to have a lot of Dutch courage to get up and dance.

Now we play music in the house and we all regularly break into song and dance in the kitchen like four lunatics. It is one of my favourite things we do as a family.

Every day I put on my runners and continue to return to nature. I recently took Hope and Joy out in their new double buggy. The lack of power steering meant to turn we had to reverse across the road and turnabout in a huge circle. This made the girls laugh, my favourite sound ever. Off we went to visit the deer on our neighbour's farm. Both girls fell asleep on the way.

As I approached the gate, I was arrested by a dozen still beings. Twenty-four eyes stared at me from stillness. There was no movement, not even blinks. I became enthralled. I stared wide-eyed. Wonderment filled me up. The hills, the fodder, and the spacious fields enveloped us in a giant green replenishing hug. Time paused. In silence and stillness, we stood staring at each other for a moment.

Suddenly the buggy began to stir. Hope woke up. She clocked the dozen deer standing on ceremony. She yelped with excitement, accompanied by kicking her legs in the air. This woke Joy up with a jump in the back seat. It scared the deer and off they ran to other side of the field.

I found myself calling out loud, 'It's ok, guys, come back. Hello, hello, hello beautiful deer.'

Joy and Hope joined in, 'Come back, mammy deer, come back, baby deer.' To my delight they did come back, all of them, as close to the fence as possible.

My mind wanted to recreate the moment of sacred silence and peace we had shared. It was gone and my busy mind took over again.

I told myself, *maybe life is simply a series of moments, some amazingly beautiful and some not so.*

We watched through the big farm gate as one gangly young deer drank milk from its mother. The doe looked tired. Her coat was a bit worn and weathered. I related to her: another tired mama. I knew neither of us would have it any other way.

Joy was full of questions and Hope smiling her toothy gummy smile from ear to ear, looking from the deer to me and back again, her eyes dancing with glee.

The sun was setting as we meandered home. We were greeted by Charlie at the door with hugs. 'We saw such wonderful deer, dear.'

He smiled at my corny joke. I could never portray the magical encounter I just had with the twenty-four eyes or the silence that spoke to me. I hoped that he already knew what I meant; the only way anyone can know life, through their own eyes.

Acknowledgements

To all of The Conrad Press team, especially my publisher, the wonderfully wise James Essinger and to Karla Harris who is a super smart editor and earth angel.

I would like to thank Rachael and Nat Ravenlock of The Book Typesetters for the amazing work they do. They really brought my vision to life by creating a book cover that captures this story and what it represents perfectly. This is a dream come true and for that I am so grateful to them both.

To Olive O' Brien who introduced me to Creative Writing on her course many years ago. To Paul Ryan who had the task of editing of the first draft of this book.

To the Thomastown Writers Group in Kilkenny where I first braved sharing my writing and Kilkenny Libraries for their support.

To Fi Connors, Homeopath and Process Worker who helped me to return to myself and to stay sane (most of the time!).

To my friends who listen and cheerlead for me. I love you all! Especially the wise woman Mary Guinan, I would be lost without you. To Rhoda Boyle my oldest friend in the world and Stephen Boyle, Karmel Dowling, Deborah Kelly, Saoirse Prendergast, Zoe Amos, Tria McGinley, Maria Ruiz Flynn, Siobhan Leonard and Michelle Keogh.

To Sara Walsh for many mystical and momentous moments on this adventure and for keeping the memory of my beautiful brother Lar alive with me.

To the loves of my life, my daughters, Amy and Chloe. They light up my world and my heart, with their very spectacular existence and my love for them.

A huge thank you to Conor, my lovely husband, who repeatedly tried to convince me *The Lotus and the Tiger* was a book before I ever dared dream it might be! He has shown me what true love is.